· SCHOLASTIC SUCCESS WITH ·

KINDERGARTEN
WORKBOOK

📖 SCHOLASTIC
Teacher
RESOURCES

Editor: Ourania Papacharalambous
Cover design by Anna Christian
Interior design by Mina Chen
Cover illustration by Rob McClurkan
Interior illustrations by: Gabriele Antonini (12, 14, 16, 18, 20, 22, 24, 26, 28, 30, 32, 34, 36, 38, 40, 42, 44, 46, 48, 50, 52, 56, 58, 60, 62, 64, 170–203); Gabriele Tafuni (162–166, 168, 169, 230–231, 236, 247, 251–252, 257–260, 274, 276, 278–279, 281, 283, 291–292, 295, 298–300, 302); Gareth Conway (13, 33, 35, 43, 45, 49, 53, 63, 74–76, 78, 82, 84, 87–88, 92, 99–100, 104, 114, 131, 133, 135, 146, 153, 155); Carol Herring (304–307, 309–314, 318, 321, 325, 329, 331, 334–337, 344, 351–353, 356, 360, 367, 372); Steve Brown (409–410); Doug Jones (spot art)
Photos @ Shutterstock.com

ISBN 978-1-338-75852-8

Scholastic Inc., 557 Broadway, New York, NY 10012
Copyright © 2021 Scholastic Inc.
All rights reserved. Printed in the U.S.A.
First printing, January 2021

3 4 5 6 7 8 9 10   144   24 23 22 21 20

TABLE OF CONTENTS

THE ALPHABET

HANDWRITING

"Nothing succeeds like success."

Alexandre Dumas the Elder, 1854

Dear Family:

Congratulations on choosing this wonderful resource for your child. For more than a century, Scholastic has been a leader in educational publishing, creating quality materials for use in schools and at home.

As a partner in your child's academic success, you'll want to take full advantage of the educational experiences offered in this book. To help your child learn at home and make the most of the opportunities in this "first" workbook, try following these helpful hints:

★ Choose a cozy place to work that is free of distractions.

★ Make sure your child has all the supplies he or she needs, such as pencils, crayons, or markers.

★ Enjoy frequent learning sessions, but keep them short. For a child in kindergarten, 10 to 15 minutes is appropriate.

★ Praise your child's successes and encourage his or her efforts. The stickers on page 441 are a great way to say, "Job well done!"

★ Offer positive support when your child needs extra help. If he or she begins to grow frustrated, take a break and revisit the topic at a later time.

★ Display your child's work and share his or her progress with family and friends.

After page 392, you'll find additional sections to complete with your child:

★ Itty-Bitty Word Books on pages 393–416 will help build your child's vocabulary.

★ The *All About Me* booklet on pages 417–432 can be removed and stapled to become a special keepsake you'll treasure for years to come.

★ The flash cards in the back of the book feature the top sight words children need to know. The flash cards are a fun way to learn the most frequently used words in reading and writing.

Take the lead and help your child succeed with the *Scholastic Success With Kindergarten Workbook!*

FOCUS SKILLS

The activities in this workbook reinforce age-appropriate skills and will help your child meet the following standards established as goals by leading educators.

Mathematics

★ Understands that numerals are symbols used to represent quantities or attributes of real-world objects

★ Counts whole numbers

★ Understands symbolic, concrete, and pictorial representations of numbers

★ Understands basic whole number relationships

★ Understands basic properties of and similarities and differences between simple geometric shapes

★ Understands the common language of spatial sense

★ Understands that geometric shapes are useful for representing and describing real-world situations

★ Extends simple patterns

Writing

★ Uses conventions of print in writing (e.g., forms letters in print, uses upper- and lowercase letters of the alphabet, writes from left-to-right and top-to-bottom)

Reading

★ Understands that print conveys meaning

★ Uses basic elements of phonetic analysis (e.g., common letter/sound relationships, beginning and ending consonants, vowel sounds, blends, word patterns) to decode unknown words

★ Uses a picture dictionary to determine word meaning

★ Understands level-appropriate sight words and vocabulary

★ Uses reading skills and strategies to understand a variety of informational texts

Science

★ Understands plants and animals and their environments

★ Recognizes weather and seasonal patterns

★ Analyzes force and motion

A Work of Art

Color each space with the letter **A** red.

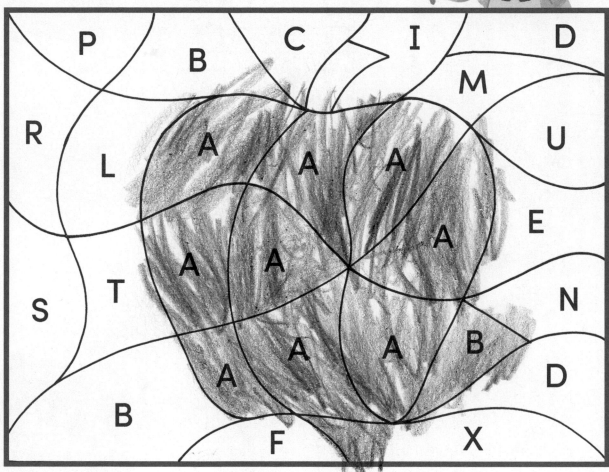

Trace and write.

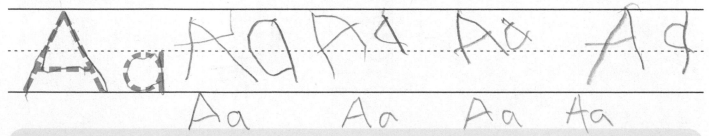

⭐ Look through a magazine for the letter **A**. How many can you find in the first 5 pages?

A

Trace the A and a's.

 Alligator paints an apple.

Now write the A and a's.

lligator paints an pple.

Add a's and then read the words.

 pple

 lligator

rm

Now write your own **Aa** word.

Aa

Big Birthday Bash!

Find and circle each **B**.

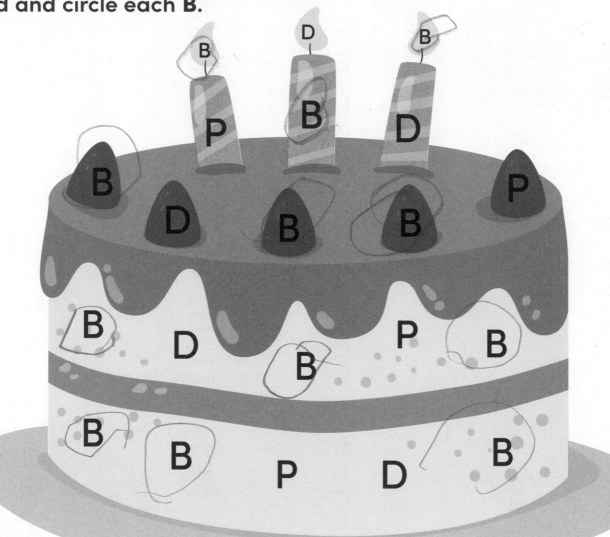

Trace and write.

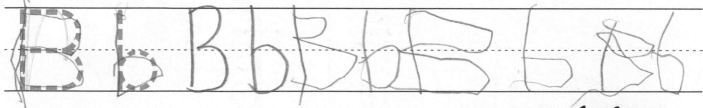

 On another sheet of paper, draw a picture of your favorite birthday present.

B

Trace the B's and b's.

Bubble Bear blows bubbles.

Now write the B's and b's.

ubble Bear blows ubbles.

Now write your own
Bb word.

Add b's and then read the words.

 ed

 ag

 ird

The King's Castle

Color the path that leads the king to the castle. Follow the letter **C**.

Trace and write.

Cat begins with the letter **C**. On another sheet of paper, draw a cat.

Trace the C and c's.

C|eo Carries Cocoa

Now write the C and c's.

|eo Carries Cocoa.

Add c's and then read the words.

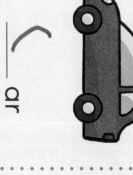
___ at

___ ar

___ ow

Now write your own
Cc word.

Dandy Duck

Color each duck track with the letter **D** orange.

Trace and write.

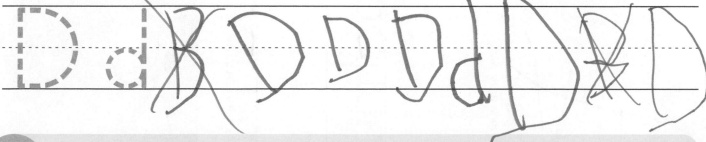

 On another sheet of paper, draw three different ducks.

Trace the D's and d.

Detective Dog likes doughnuts.

Now write the D's and d.

etective ___og likes ___oughnuts.

etective ___og likes ___oughnuts.

Add d's and then read the words.

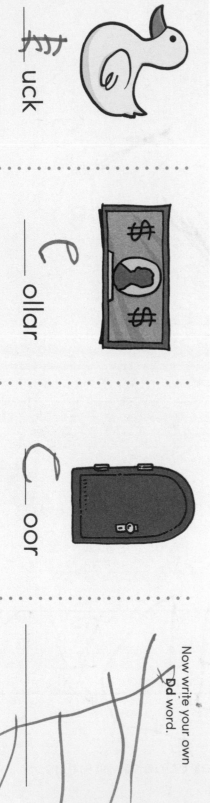

___uck

___ollar

___oor

Now write your own **Dd** word.

Eggs Everywhere!

Find and color each egg with the letter **E**.

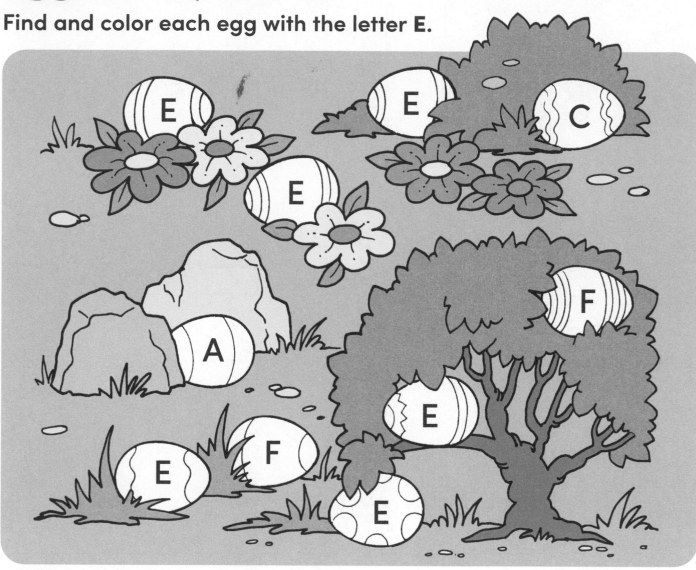

Trace and write.

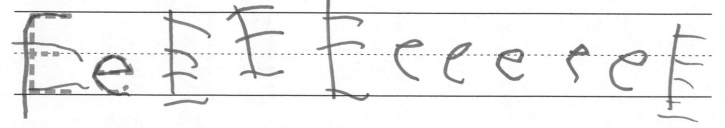

 On another sheet of paper, draw and color two decorated eggs.

E

Trace the E's and e.

E̲ vin E̲ ephant makes an e.

Now write the E's and e.

̲vin ̲ephant makes an ̲.

̲vin ̲ephant makes an ̲.

Now write your own
Ee word.

Add e's and then read the words.

—— lbow

—— ye

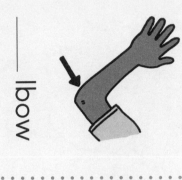

—— gg

In Full Bloom

Color each space with the letter **F** yellow.
Color all the other spaces blue.

Trace and write.

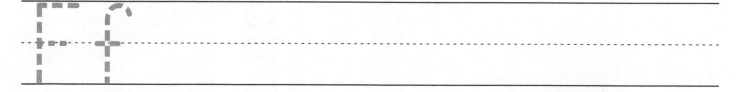

 Flower begins with the letter **F**. On another
sheet of paper, draw a red flower.

Trace the F's and f.

Fifi the Ferret plays the flute.

Now write the F's and f.

___ifi the ___erret plays the ___lute.

Add f's and then read the words.

Now write your own **Ff** word.

___ erret plays the ___ lute.

___eather

___ish

___ork

A Grape-Eating Gorilla

Color the path that leads the gorilla to the grapes.
Follow the letter **G**.

Trace and write.

Trace the G and g's.

G orilla g obbles g ooseberries.

Now write the G and g's.

____ orilla ____ obbles ____ ooseberries.

Now write your own
Gg word.

_____

Add g's and then read the words.

____ ame

____ uitar

____ ate

Hippo's Hats

Color each hat with the letter **H**.

Trace and write.

On another sheet of paper, draw a picture of a word that rhymes with *hat*.

H

Trace the H's and h.

Harry Hippo is hiding.

Now write the H's and h.

_arry _ippo is _iding.

_arry _ippo is _iding.

Add h's and then read the words.

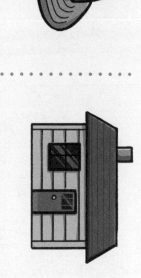

___ air   ___ at   ___ ouse

Now write your own
Hh word.

_____

Icky Insects!

Color each insect with the letter **I**.

Trace and write.

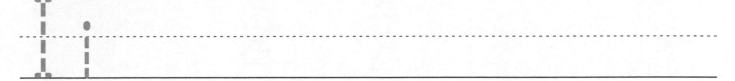

On another sheet of paper, draw a picture of something you think is icky.

I I

Trace the I and i's.

I guana is on the iceberg.

Now write the I and i's.

_guana_s on the _ceberg.

Add i's and then read the words.

___ ce cream

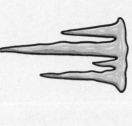

___ cicle

___ ron

Now write your own
Ii word.

Jelly Beans

Color each jelly bean with the letter **J**.

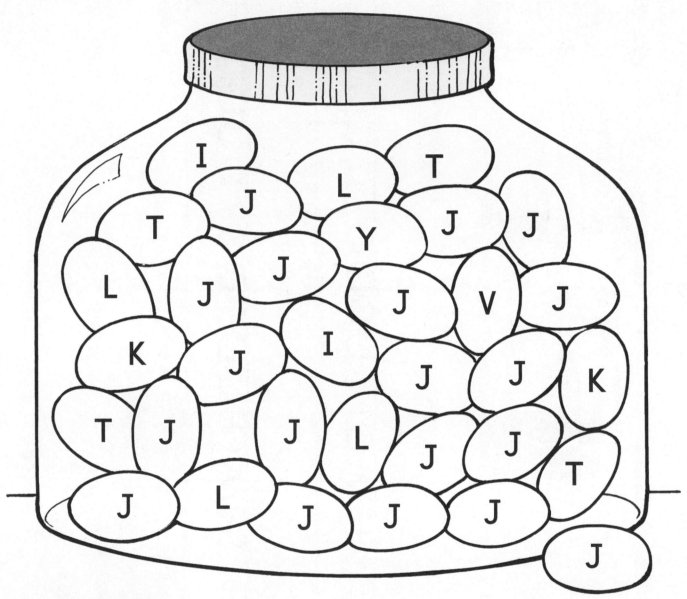

Trace and write.

J

Trace the J's and j.

Jonah Jaguar loves jam.

Now write the J's and j.

_____onah _____aguar loves _____am.

Add j's and then read the words.

Now write your own Jj word.

_____ar

_____ump

_____eans

Colorful Kites

Draw a line from each kite with the letter **K** to the boy.
Color each kite with the letter **K**.

Trace and write.

 On another sheet of paper, draw a picture of a beautiful kite.

Trace the K and k.

Kangaroo plays kazoo.

Now write the K and k.

kangaroo plays kazoo.

Now write your own
Kk word.

Add k's and then read the words.

_____ ing

_____ ite

_____ angaroo

Check It Out!

Find and circle each L hidden in the picture.

Trace and write.

 Check out a book from the library.

L

Trace the L's and l's.

Lois Lamb loves to laugh.

Now write the L's and l's.

Lois Lamb loves to laugh.

Add l's and then read the words.

L emon

L eaf

L ion

Now write your own Ll word.

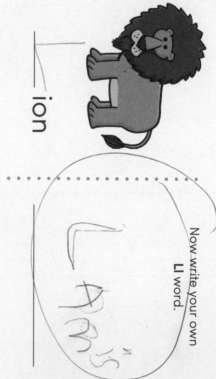

Musical Mouse

Color the path that leads the mouse to the mandolin.
Follow the letter **M**.

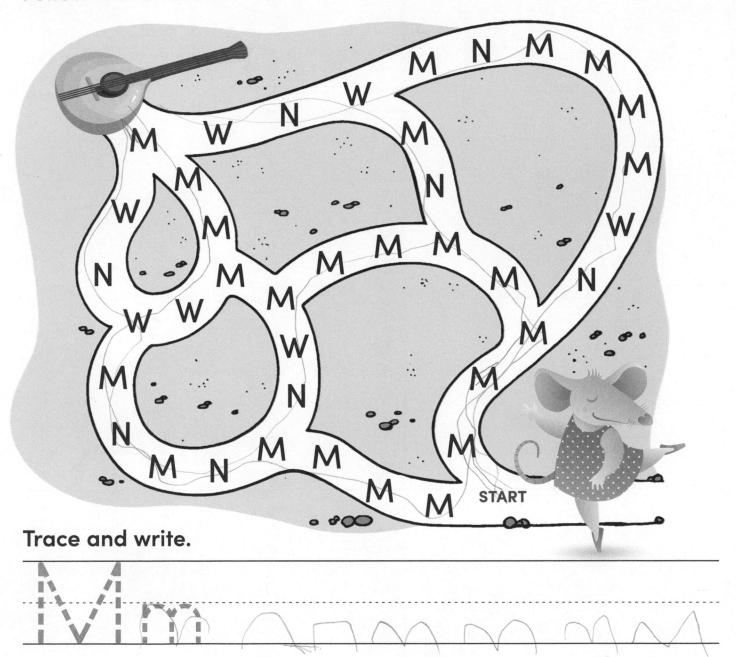

Trace and write.

 On another sheet of paper, draw a picture of a mouse house.

M

Trace the M's and m's.

Matt Monkey mops milk.

Now write the M's and m's.

att

onkey

mops

milk.

Now write your own Mm word.

_____

Add m's and then read the words.

____ouse

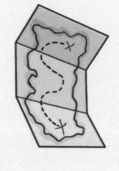

____ap

____onkey

Noodle Doodle Soup

Color each **N** in the bowl of soup.

Trace and write.

N

Trace the N's and n.

Nate Newt has a nickel.

Now write the N's and n.

Nate Newt has a nickel.

Add n's and then read the words.

_est

_ewspaper

_ut

Now write your own
Nn word.

What Is Ollie?

Color each space with the letter **O** purple.
Color all the other spaces blue.

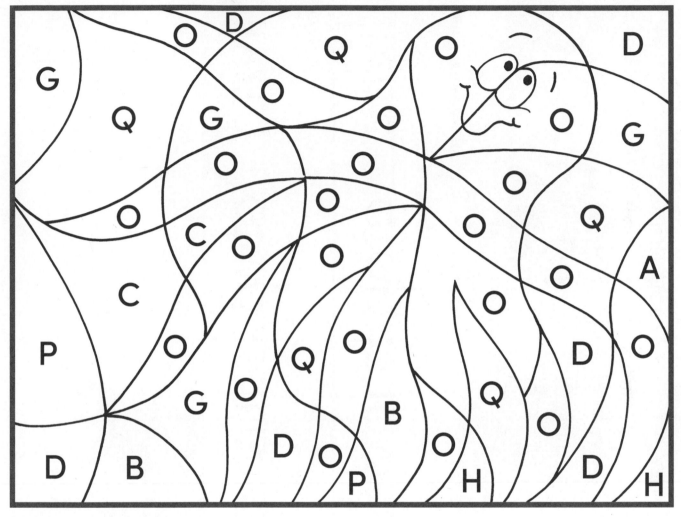

Trace and write.

 Orange begins with the letter **O**. On another sheet of paper, draw an orange.

Trace the O's and o.

 live ctopus loves nions.

Now write the O's and o.

live ctopus loves nions.

Add o's and then read the words.

 wl

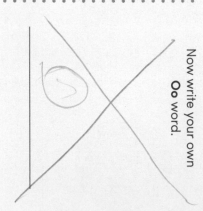 ctopus

 ven

Now write your own **Oo** word.

Plenty of Popcorn

Help Pete find his popcorn.
Color each piece of popcorn with the letter **P**.

Trace and write.

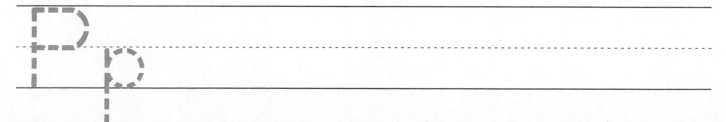

P

Trace the P and p's.

The Parks planned a picnic.

Now write the P and p's.

The __arks __anned a __icnic.

Now write your own **Pp** word.

Add p's and then read the words.

____ail

____encil

____an

The Queen's Quilt

Color each space with the letter **Q** yellow.
Color all the other spaces green.

Trace and write.

Trace the Q's and q.

Quincy Quail likes quiet.

Now write the Q's and q.

_uincy _____ uail likes _____ uiet.

Add q's and then read the words.

_____ ueen

_____ uilt

SHHH

_____ uiet

Now write your own **Qq** word.

_____

Raindrops

Find and circle each **R** on the umbrella.
Color each raindrop with the letter **R** blue.

Trace and write.

R r

 Rainbow begins with the letter **R**. On another sheet of paper, draw a rainbow.

R

Trace the R's and r's.

Rosie Rabbit rakes rocks.

Now write the R's and r's.

___osie ___abbit ___akes ___ocks.

Now write your own
Rr word.

_____

Add r's and then read the words.

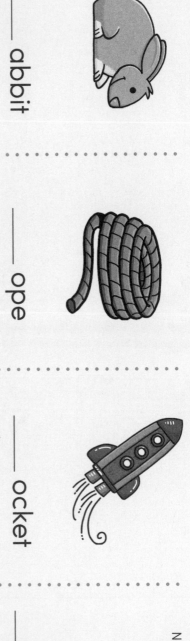

___abbit   ___ope   ___ocket

Building a Sandcastle

Find and circle each S in the sandcastle.

Trace and write.

Ss

 Sandwich begins with the letter **S**. On another sheet of paper, draw a picture of your favorite sandwich.

S

Trace the S and s.

Seal makes a sandwich.

Now write the S and s.

_____eal makes a _andwich.

Add s's and then read the words.

_____andwich

_____ock

_____oap

Now write your own
Ss word.

Fast Track

Color the path that leads Tommy Train to the station.
Follow the letter **T**.

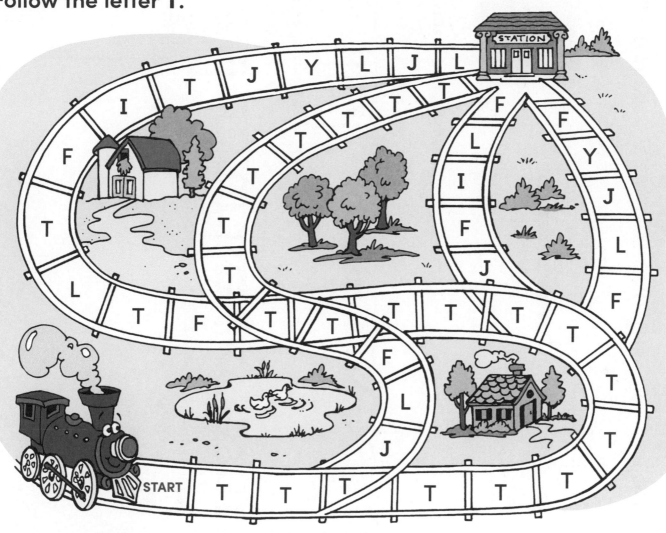

Trace and write.

  Turtle begins with the letter **T**. On another sheet of paper, draw a picture of a turtle.

Trace the T's and t's.

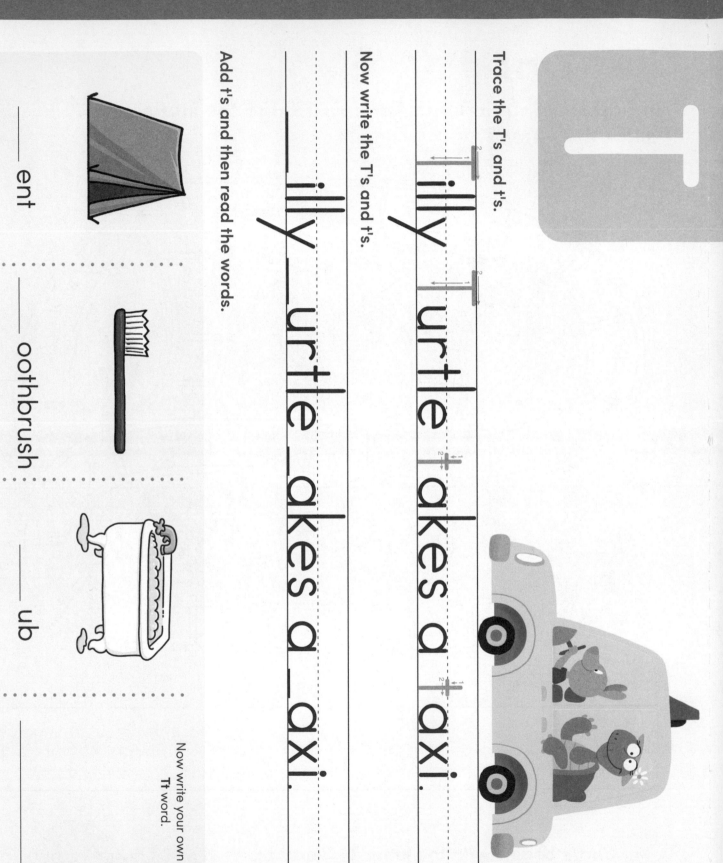

T

Tilly Turtle takes a taxi.

Now write the T's and t's.

_illy _urtle _akes a _axi.

Add t's and then read the words.

___ent

___oothbrush

___ub

Now write your own Tt word.

Under the Umbrella

Find and circle each U in the picture.

Trace and write.

Under begins with the letter **U**. On another sheet of paper, draw a picture of something hiding under a shell.

Trace the U and u.

Umbrellabird rides a unicycle.

Now write the U and u.

mbrellabird rides a _____nicycle.

Now write your own **Uu** word.

Add u's and then read the words.

_____mbrella

_____nicorn

_____p

Voting for Veggies

Color each veggie with the letter **V** green.

Trace and write.

 Veggie begins with the letter **V**. On another sheet of paper, draw your two favorite veggies.

Trace the V's and v.

Vera Viper has a valentine.

Now write the V's and v.

_era _iper has a _alentine.

Add v's and then read the words.

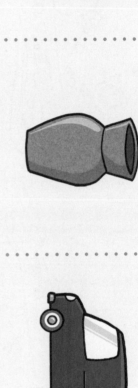

___est

___ase

___an

Now write your own
Vv word.

_____

Guess Who?

Color each space with the letter **W** green.
Color all the other spaces brown.

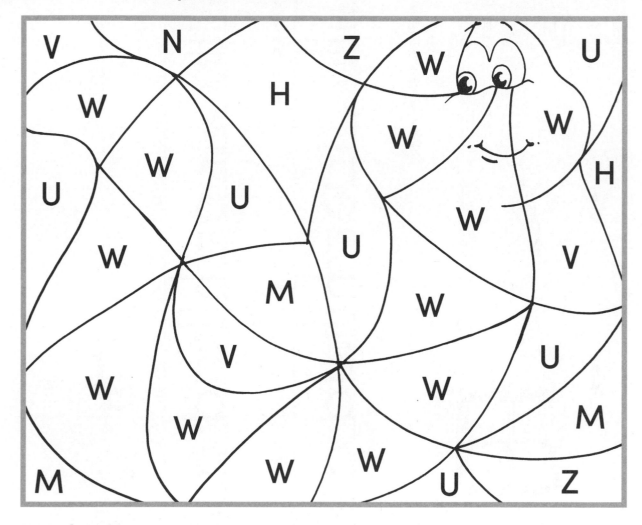

Trace and write.

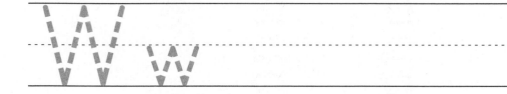

 Whale begins with the letter **W**. On another sheet of paper, draw a big whale.

Trace the W's and w.

W W W

W W W

Now write the W's and w.

Willy Worm had a wagon.

_illy _orm had a _agon.

_orm had a _agon.

Add w's and then read the words.

___eb

___orm

___indow

Now write your own **Ww** word.

_____

X Marks the Spot!

Help the girl find her way to the treasure chest.
Follow the letter **X**.

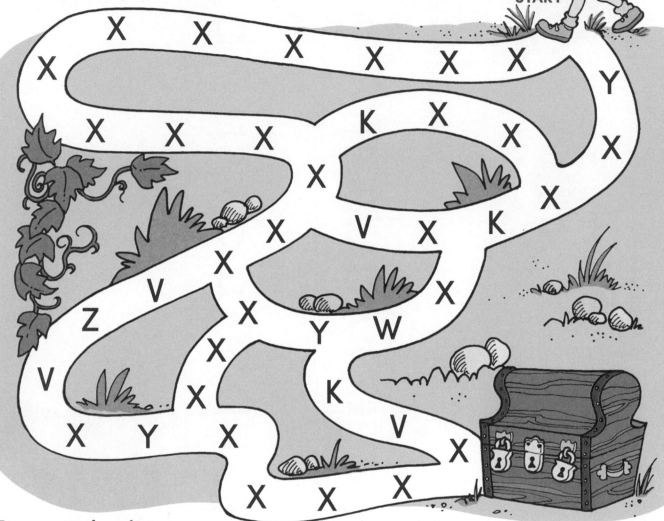

Trace and write.

⭐ On another sheet of paper, draw five *X*'s in a row.

Trace the X and x.

X

X –ray fish plays a xylophone.

Now write the X and x.

___ –ray fish plays a _ylophone.

___ –ray fish plays a _ylophone.

Now write your own
Xx word.

Add x's and then read the words.

fo_____

___ylophone

___–ray

Yummy Yogurt

Color each space with the letter **Y** yellow.
Color all the other spaces green.

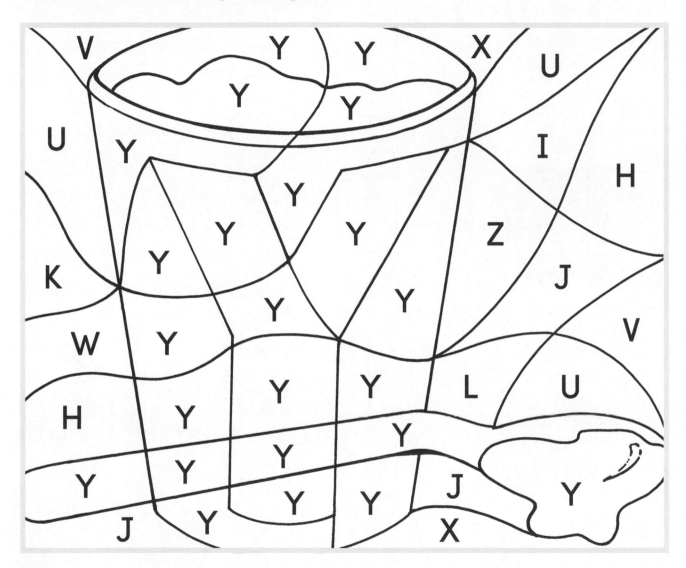

Trace and write.

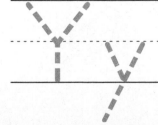

Trace the Y's and y.

Y ana Y ak ate y ogurt.

Now write the Y's and y.

ana ak ate ogurt.

Add y's and then read the words.

Now write your own
Yy word.

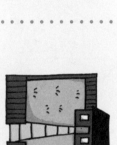

—— arn

—— ard

—— o-yo

Zany Zookeeper

Find and circle each **Z** in the picture.

Zebras

Zoo

Trace and write.

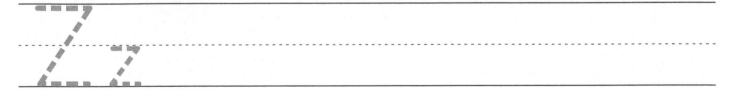

Zero begins with the letter **Z**. On another sheet of paper, draw five zeroes in a row.

Z

Trace the Z's and z.

Zed Z ebra lives at the zoo.

Now write the Z's and z.

ed ebra lives at the oo.

Add z's and then read the words.

ebra

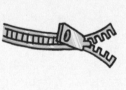

ero

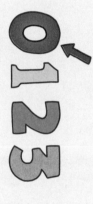

ipper

Now write your own
Zz word.

Band of Ants

Color each drum with the letter **a** red.
Color each drum with the letter **b** blue.
Color each drum with the letter **c** green.

Trace and write.

a b c

 On another sheet of lined paper, write the letters **Aa**, **Bb**, and **Cc**.

Dinosaur Dig

Follow the letters **d**, **e**, and **f** in order.
Color the path that leads to the dinosaur bones.

START

e d f e d f e d d
e d e d
f e d
d e f
e d f
f e d
f d e
e d d
e f d e f d e f

Trace and write.

d e f

Look in a magazine to find the letters **d**, **e**, and **f**.

Inch by Inch

To find out what insect moves about an inch at a time, color each space with the letter **g** orange. Color each space with the letter **h** yellow. Color each space with the letter **i** black.

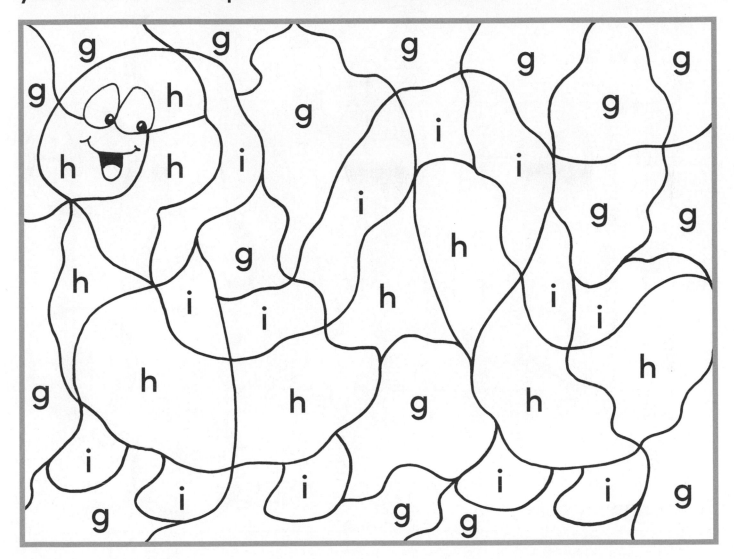

Trace and write.

Kicking Kangaroos

Draw a line from each kangaroo to the soccer balls with the same letter.

Trace and write.

j   k   l

Ocean of Letters

Find and circle the letters **m**, **n**, and **o** in the picture.

Trace and write.

 On another sheet of lined paper, write the letters **m**, **n**, and **o** with their matching capital letters.

Plenty of Penguins

Circle each penguin with the letter **p**. Mark an **X** on each penguin with the letter **q**. Underline each penguin with the letter **r**.

Trace and write.

Spotted Turtle

Color each space with the letters **s**, **t**, or **u** to find a hidden letter.

s	u	u	w
t	f	c	m
u	s	s	a
f	w	t	w
t	s	u	f

Trace and write.

s t u

 On another sheet of lined paper, write **Ss**, **Tt**, and **Uu**.

Watermelon Fun

Color each seed with the letters **v**, **w**, or **x** black.

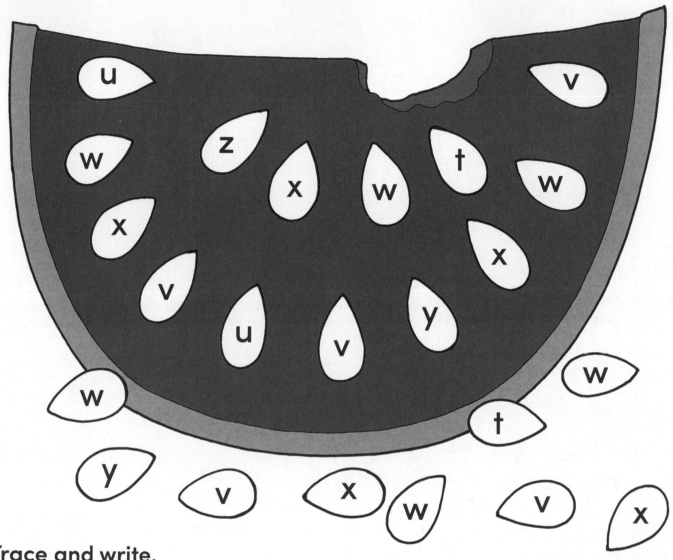

Trace and write.

 On another sheet of paper, draw a picture of your favorite fruit.

Follow the Yellow Brick Road

Color the road that leads from the yak to the zoo.
Follow the letters **y** and **z**.

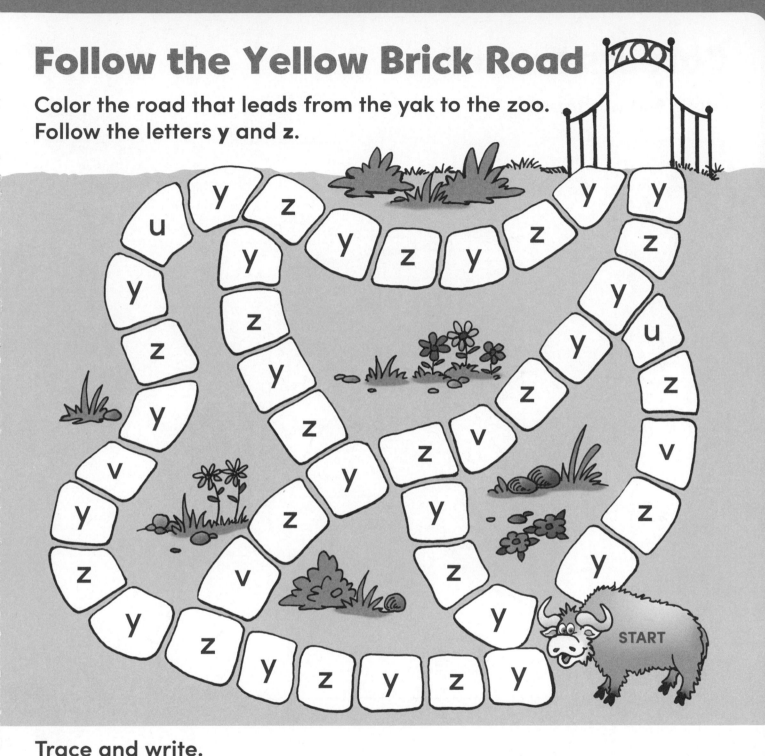

Trace and write.

y z

Careers From A to Z

Finish the alphabet.

On another sheet of paper, draw a picture of what you would like to be when you grow up.

Lost and Found

Find and circle each uppercase letter of the alphabet in the picture.

A B C D E F G H I J K L M
N O P Q R S T U V W X Y Z

 Circle the letter your name begins with in the letter box above.

ABC Picture

Connect the dots in ABC order to find the hidden picture.
Tell a story about the picture.

Write It Right!

Write the missing lowercase letters.

Playing in the Park

Find and circle each lowercase letter of the alphabet in the picture.
Say the letters as you find them.

Letters on Parade

Connect the dots from **a** to **z**.

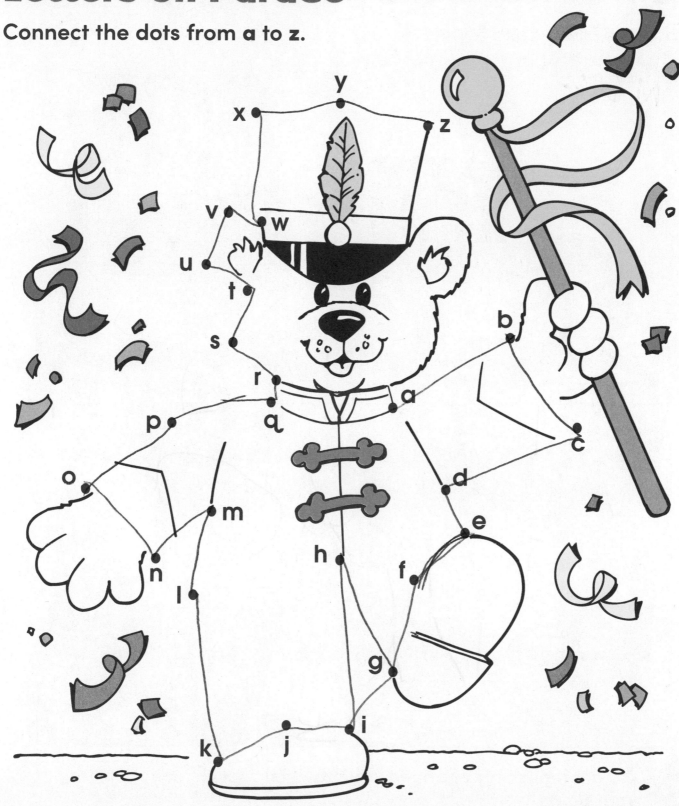

Be a Better Builder

Write the lowercase letter.

N 60%

A _____ F _____

D _____ G _____ J _____

L _____ N _____ P _____

S _____ U _____ W _____

Y _____ K _____ Q _____

O _____ B _____ R _____

 On another sheet of paper, write the first and last letters of your name.

Match and Learn

Draw a line from each uppercase letter to its matching
lowercase letter.

B 84%

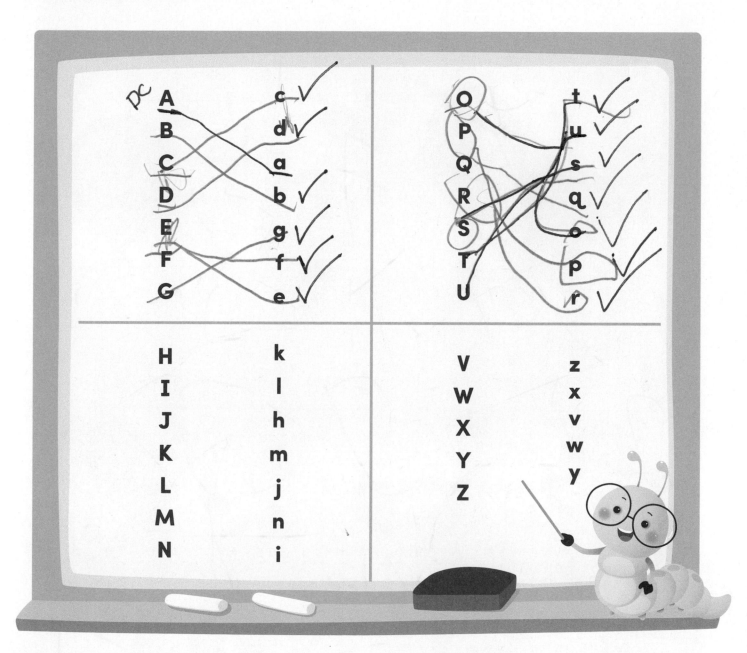

A	c
B	d
C	a
D	b
E	g
F	f
G	e

O	t
P	u
Q	v
R	s
S	q
T	o
U	p
	r

H	k
I	l
J	h
K	m
L	j
M	n
N	i

V	z
W	x
X	v
Y	w
Z	y

What are the names of each person in your home? Write the first
letter of each person's name on another sheet of paper.

Clowning Around

Match the letter on each clown to the balloon with its lowercase letter.

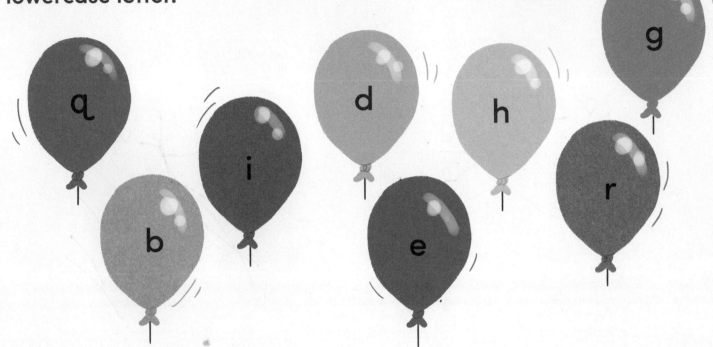

NUMBERS AND COUNTING

Zero at the Zoo

Trace and write.

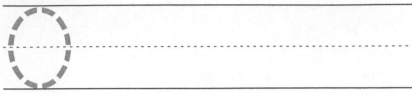

0

Circle the number that tells how many.

bears
0 1 2 3 4

birds
0 1 2 3 4

penguins
0 1 2 3 4

lions
0 1 2 3 4

camels
0 1 2 3 4

ducks
0 1 2 3 4

monkeys
0 1 2 3 4

seals
0 1 2 3 4

One Old Octopus

Trace and write.

Color each shape with 1 fish.

An Underwater Home

Count each group of things found in the sea. Color one of each.

 How many objects did you color? _____

Two Talking Turtles

Trace and write.

2

Color each circle with 2 dots.

 Count how many phones are in your home.

Mrs. Tacky Turtle

Circle the number that tells how many.

	1	2
	1	2
	1	2
	1	2
	1	2
	1	2
0	1	2

 What else could Mrs. Turtle wear? Draw 2 of them on Mrs. Turtle.

Three Tiny Tugboats

Trace and write.

3

Color each barge with 3 objects.

Draw 3 logs on each barge.

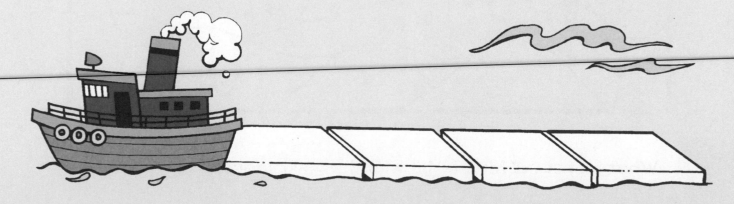

Tugboat Tow

Use the color key to color the picture.

 **blue**   2  **brown**   3 **red**

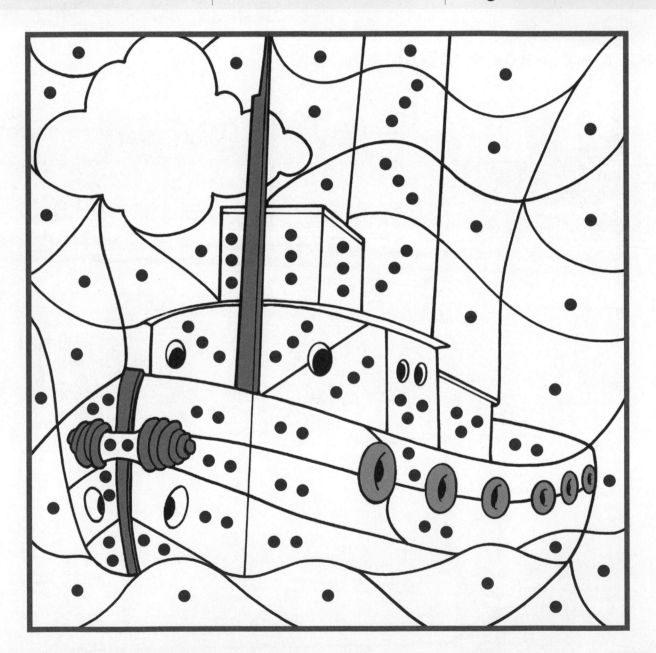

 Which color did you use to color the most spaces? _____

Four Fine Firefighters

Trace and write.

4

Color each dog with 4 spots.

Climb to the Top

Count the objects on each step. Circle the matching number.

 How many steps have 4 objects? _____

Five Friendly Frogs

Trace and write.

5

Color each lily pad with 5 flies.

Fast Frogs

Color each rock with 5 bugs to find which frog finishes first.

 How many rocks have 4 bugs? _____

Six Smelly Shoes

Trace and write.

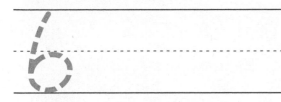

Circle 6 shoes in each box.

Draw more shoes to make 6.

How many socks are there? Circle the number.   5   6   7

Two Make a Pair

Count the shapes on each shoe.
Draw a line to the matching number.

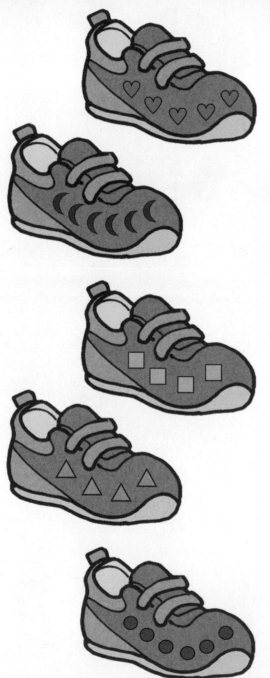

 Count all of your shoes. How many did you count? _____

Seven Seashells

Trace and write.

7

Color 7 shells in each box.

Seashells by the Seashore

Count each kind of shell in the picture.
Circle the shells that total 7.

How many of each did you find in the picture? Write the number.

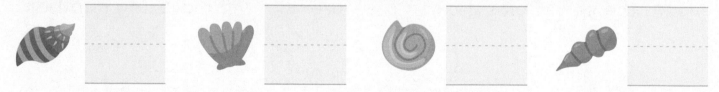

Circle the number that tells how many.

© Scholastic Inc.

Eight Electric Eels

Trace and write.

8

Draw more eels to make 8.

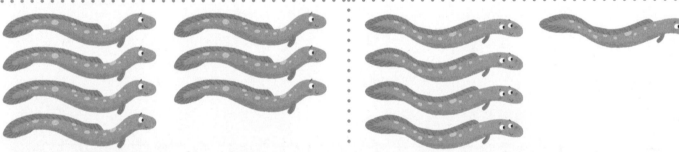

Count the eels. Color the sea creature with the matching number.

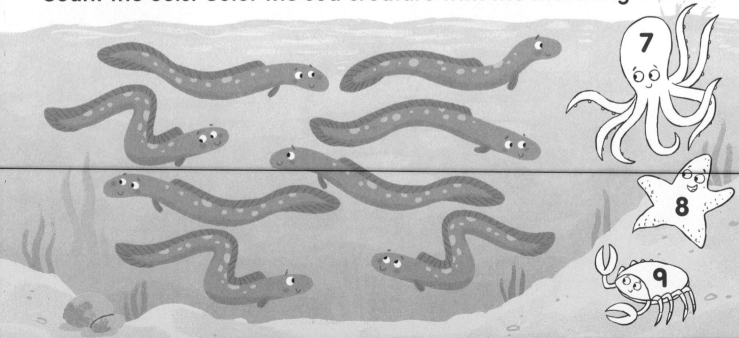

Eddie Eel Is Lost

Help Eddie Eel find his way back to the cave.
Trace the path that goes in order from 1 to 8.

 On another sheet of paper, draw a picture of 8 different sea creatures.

© Scholastic Inc.

Nine Nice Nectarines

Trace and write.

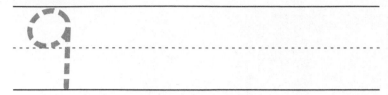

Color each basket that has 9 pieces of fruit.

Going to the Market

Count. Write how many. Color each group with 9 pieces of fruit.

 On another sheet of paper, draw 9 pieces of your favorite fruit.

Ten Railroad Ties

Trace and write.

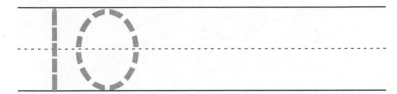

Help Tina Train find the right track. Count each railroad tie.
Color the track with 10 railroad ties red.

All Aboard

Color each train car with 8 barrels red.
Color each train car with 9 barrels blue.
Color each train car with 10 barrels green.

 On another sheet of paper, draw a train with 10 train cars.

1, 2... Presents for You!

Draw a circle around each group of 1.
Draw a square around each group of 2.

3, 4 ... Let's Read More!

Draw a triangle around each group of 3.
Draw a diamond around each group of 4.

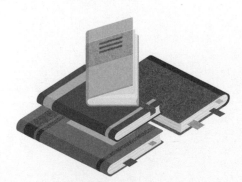

5, 6... Flowers to Pick!

Draw an oval around each group of 5.
Draw a rectangle around each group of 6.

7, 8... Time to Skate!

Color each group of 7 red. Color each group of 8 yellow.

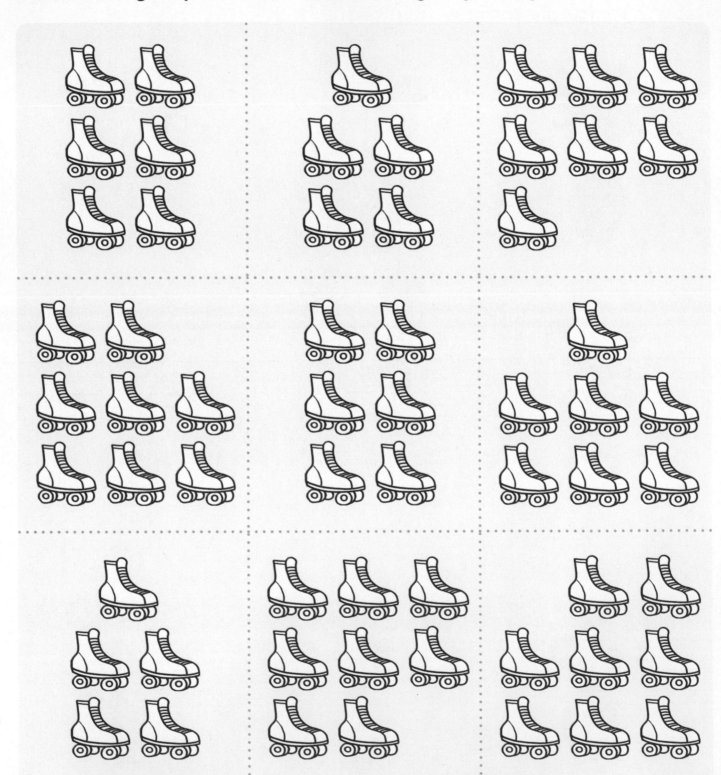

© Scholastic Inc.

9, 10... It's Fun to Win!

Color each group of 9 blue. Color each group of 10 green.

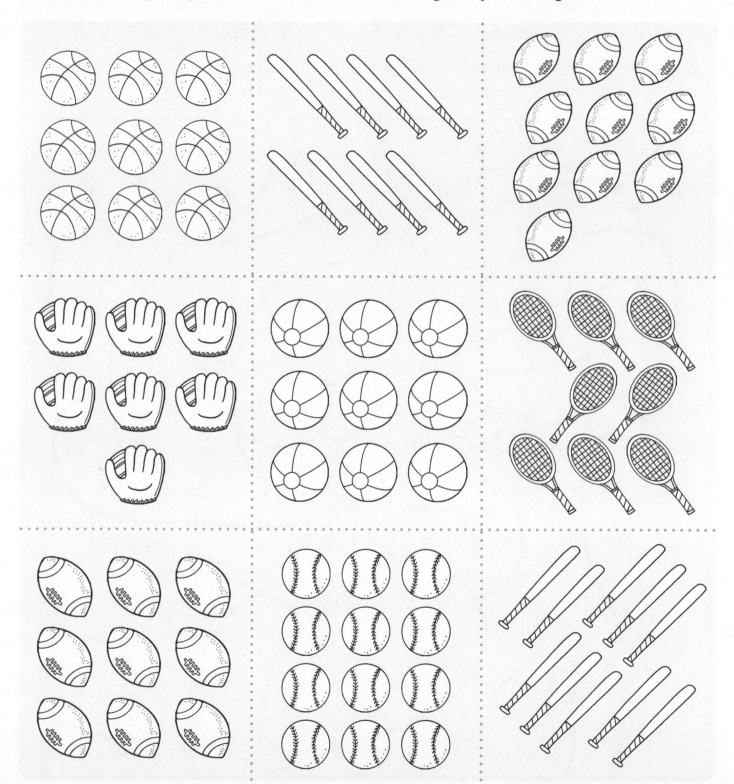

Bunny Number Fun

Use the color key to color the picture.

1 pink	**2** green	**3** blue	**4** red	**5** brown
6 yellow	**7** purple	**8** black	**9** orange	

A Colorful Garden

Use the color key to color the picture.

• yellow	: pink	⦙ red	:: black	∴: orange
:: purple	⁖: blue	:::: green	⁙ brown	

Gumball Goodies

Use the color key to color the picture.

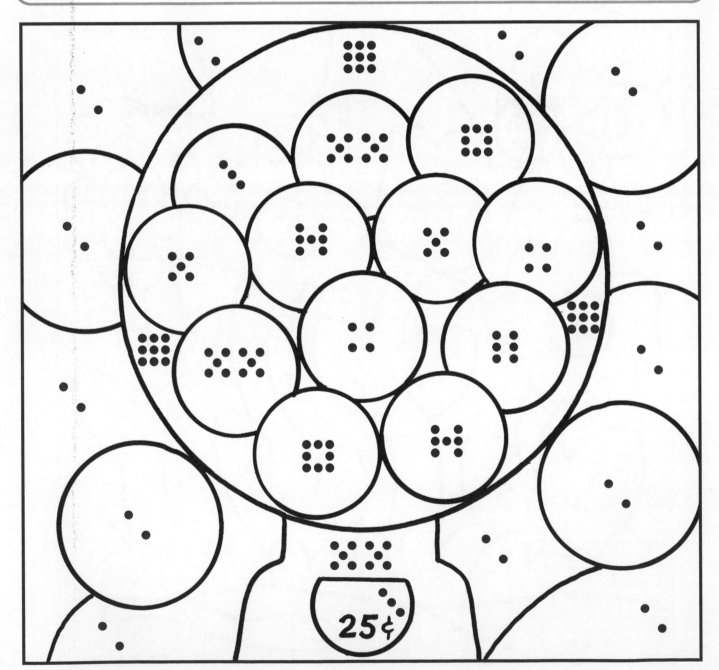

Count and Color

Color the correct number of objects in each row.

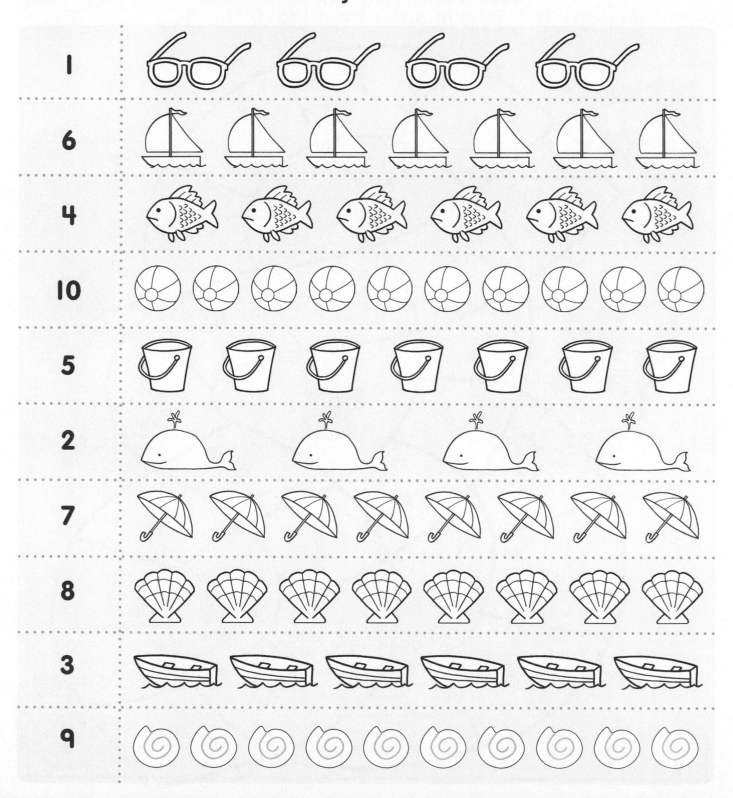

Calling All Alarms

Help the fire truck get to the fire.
Color the path that goes in order from 1 to 10.

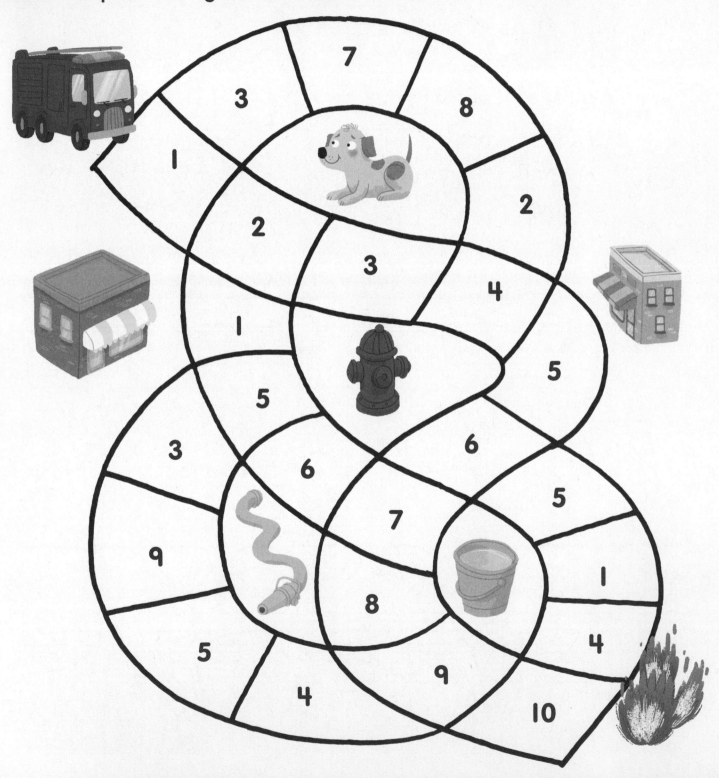

© Scholastic Inc.

Eleven Excited Earthworms

Trace and write.

Color each set of 11 earthworms.

Betty Bookworm

Count each stack of books. Draw a line to match each stack to the correct number.

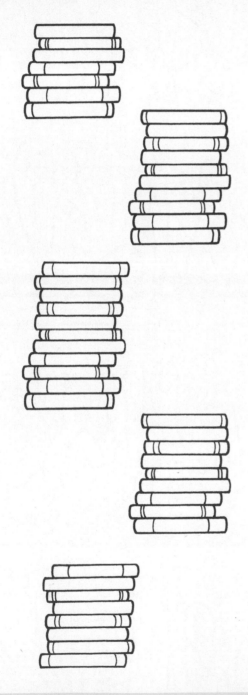

 Color the stack with 11 books.

Twelve Tasty Treats

Trace and write.

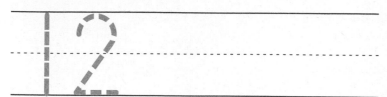

Count the candy in each jar. Color each jar with 12.

Gingerbread Man

Help the Gingerbread Man find his gingerbread house. Color the path that goes in order from 1 to 12.

8   7   6   5   4   3   2   1

3   2

4   3

5   4   4

6   7   6   5   5   6

8   6   7

9   7

10   10   9   8

11   9   8

12

How many objects did you color? _____

© Scholastic Inc.

Thirteen Tasty Treats

Trace and write.

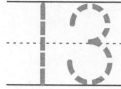

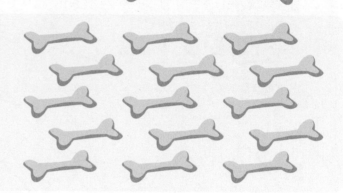

Circle 13 treats in each picture.

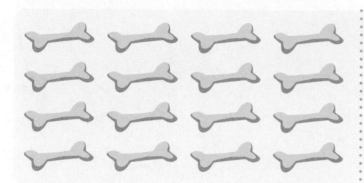

Draw more treats to make 13.

Count the treats. Circle the correct number.   12   13   14

Where, Oh Where, Has My Puppy Gone?

Help the puppy find its home.
Draw a line along the path that goes in order from 1 to 13.

Write the number that comes next in each treat.

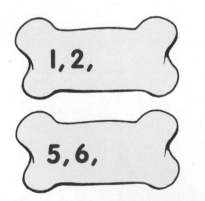

1, 2,

7, 8,

11, 12,

5, 6,

9, 10,

4, 5,

Juggling Fourteen Balls

Trace and write.

14

Color each ball with 14 dots.

Catch the Ball!

Count. Write how many.

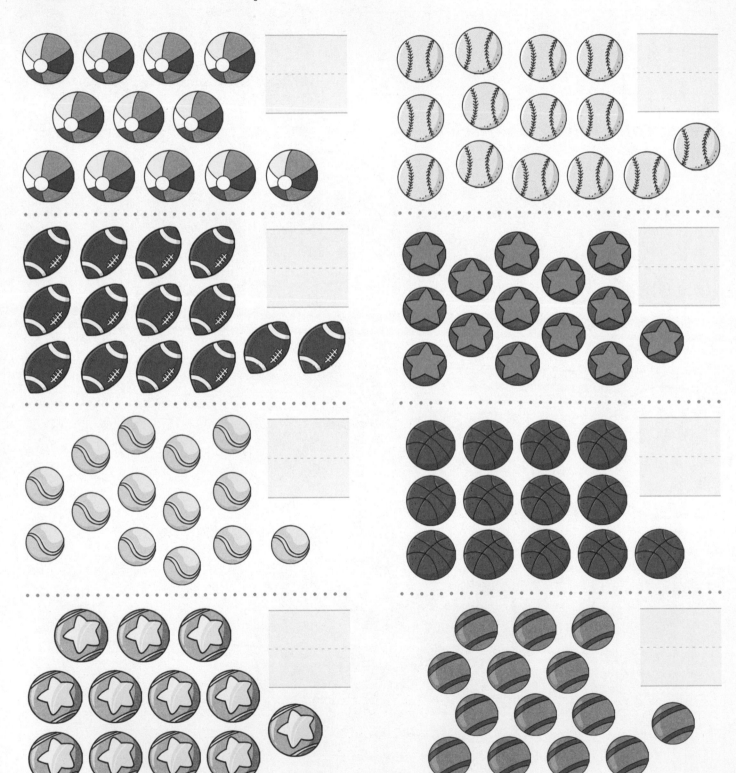

Fifteen Pennies

Trace and write.

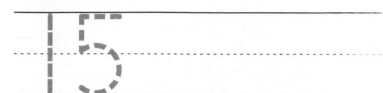

Count the pennies in each bank. Color each bank with 15 pennies.

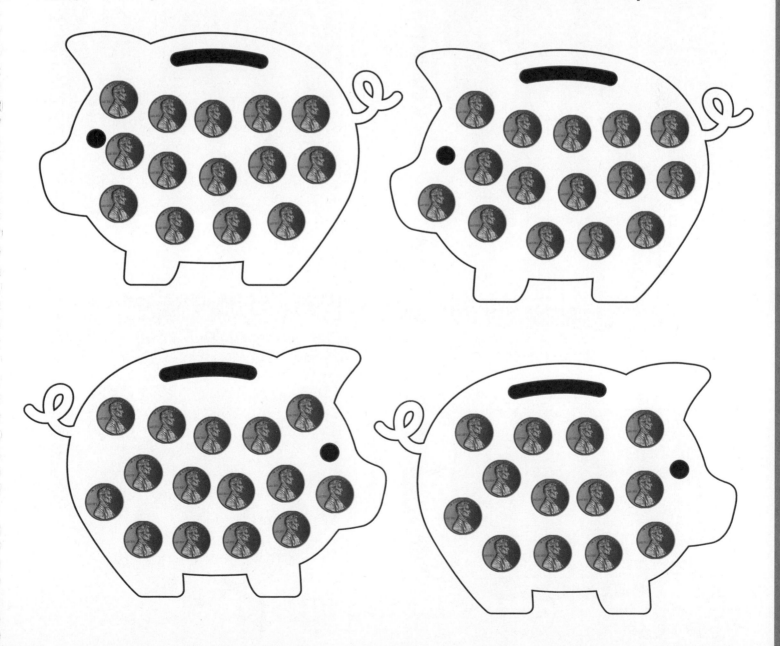

A Penny in Your Pocket

A penny equals 1¢. Count the pennies in each pocket.
Write the total.

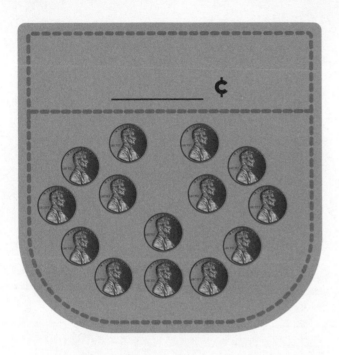 

Sixteen Kites

Trace and write.

16

Count the bows on each tail. Color each kite with 16 bows.

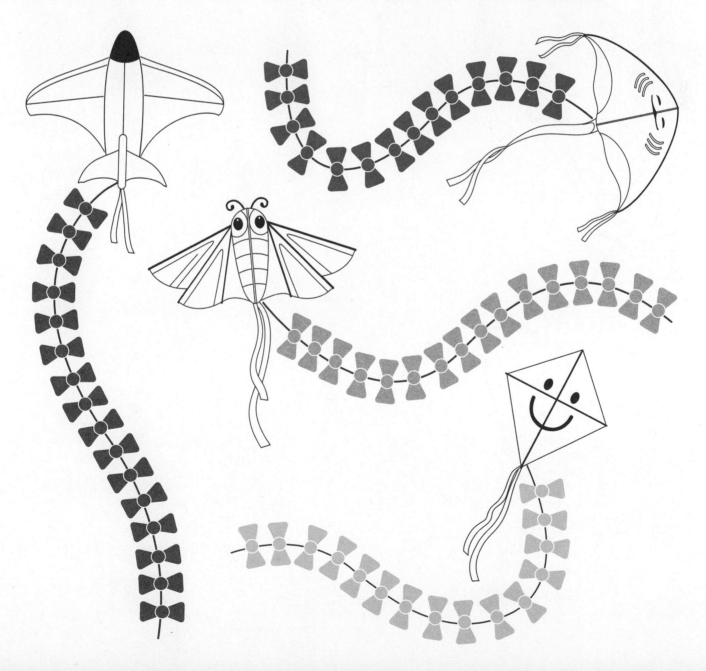

Flying High

Connect the dots from 1 to 16. Color the picture.

Count. Write how many.

Seventeen Gallons of Gas

Trace and write.

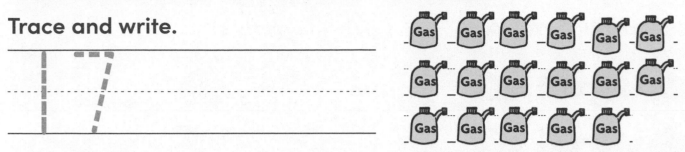

Find the gas pump by following the numbers in order from 1 to 17.

Way to Go!

Count. Write how many.

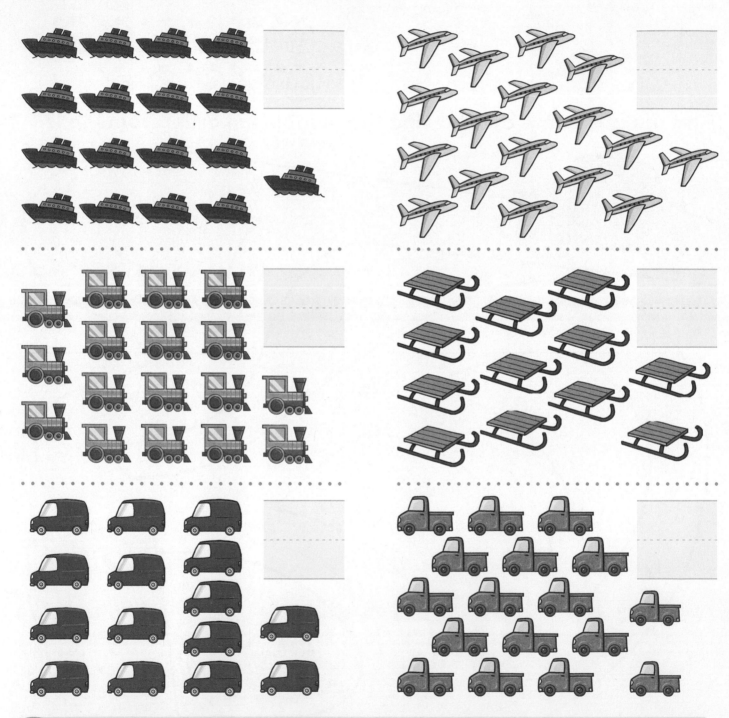

Eighteen Stars

Trace and write.

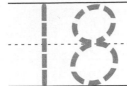

Circle 18 stars in each picture.

Draw more stars to make 18.

Count the planets. Write the number. _____

Out of This World

Count. Color each group of 18 objects.

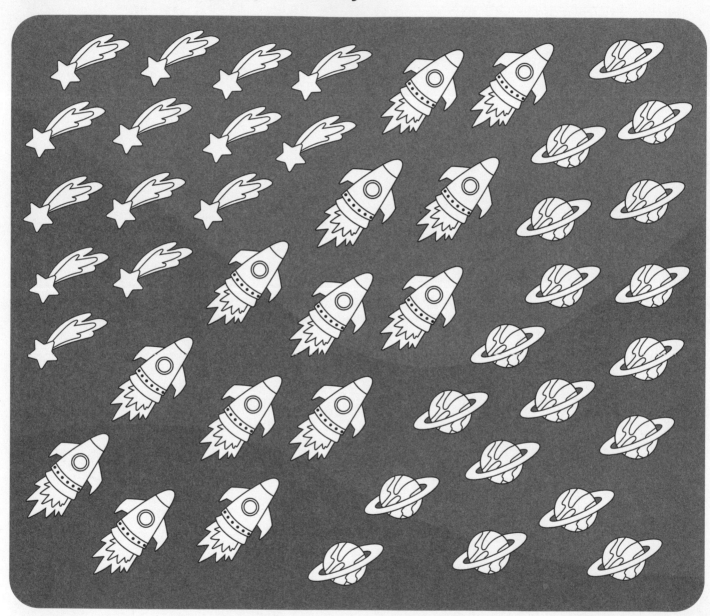

Write how many of each object you found.

Nineteen Marbles

Trace and write.

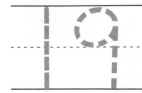

Circle the number that tells how many.
Color each group with 19 marbles.

17   18   19

17   18   19

17   18   19

17   18   19

17   18   19

17   18   19

Let's Play Marbles!

Circle 19 marbles.

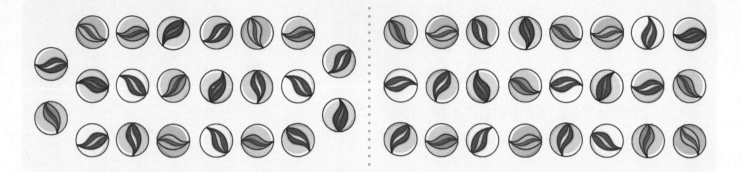

Draw more marbles to make 19.

Count the marbles. Write the number.

Twenty Butterflies to Count

Trace and write.

20

Write the numbers 1 to 20 on the trail.
Then, find and color 20 butterflies in the picture.

Don't Bug Me!

Count each group of bugs. Draw a line to the matching numbers.

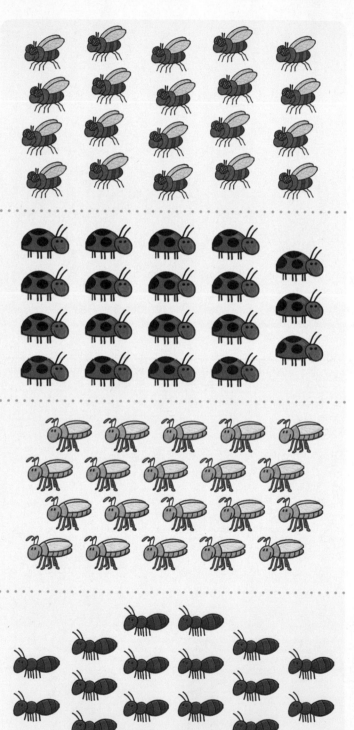

19

20

18

20

Scholastic Success With Kindergarten

11, 12 . . . It's on the Shelf!

Draw a circle around each group of 11.
Draw a square around each group of 12.

13, 14 . . . Let's Play the Tambourine!

Draw an oval around each group of 13.
Draw a rectangle around each group of 14.

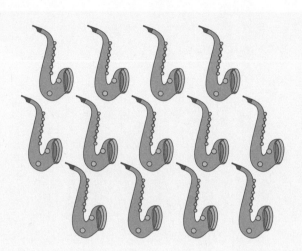

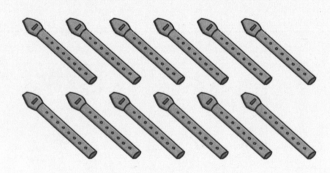

15, 16 . . . Eat Your Peas!

Draw a circle around each group of 15.
Draw a rectangle around each group of 16.

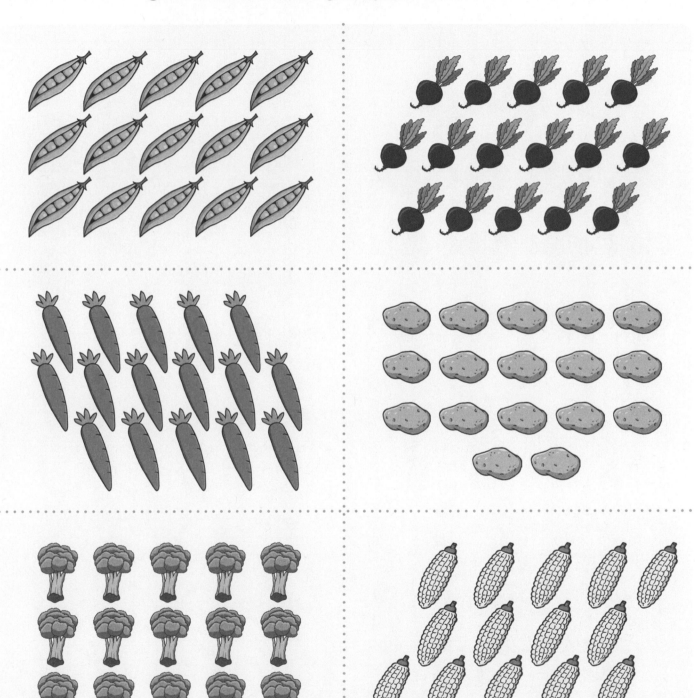

17, 18 . . . Don't Forget the Sunscreen!

Draw a circle around each group of 17.
Draw a square around each group of 18.

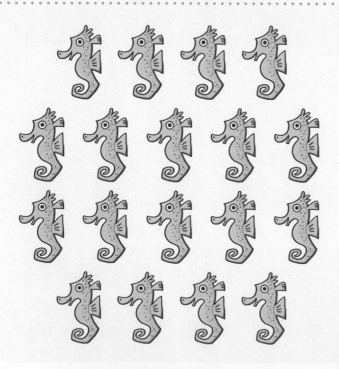

19, 20 . . . There Are Plenty!

Draw a circle around each group of 19.
Draw a square around each group of 20.

Time to Build

Use the color key to color the picture.

| 11 yellow | 12 black | 13 blue | 14 white | 15 orange |
| 16 green | 17 red | 18 purple | 19 brown | 20 pink |

Let's Count!

Color the correct number of objects in each row.

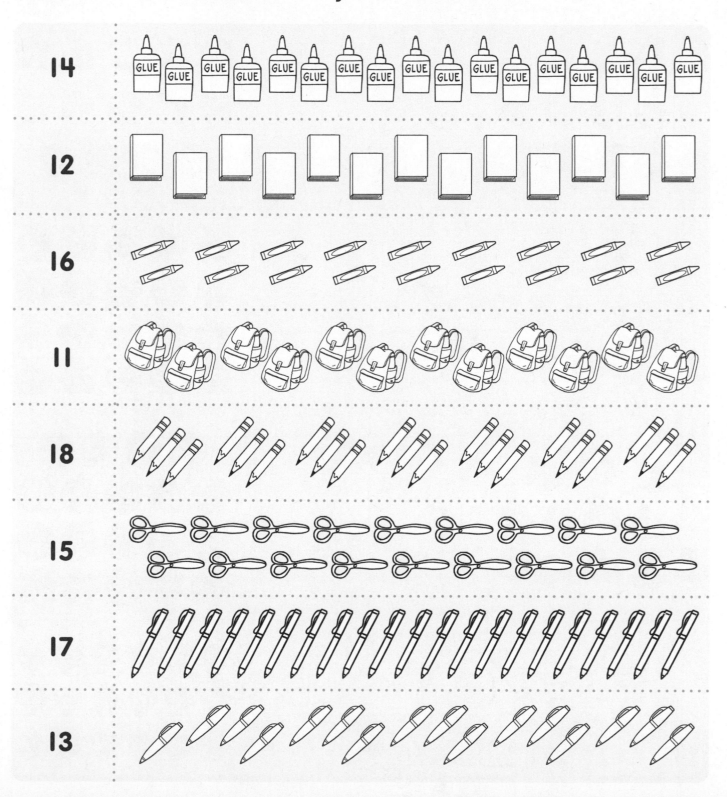

14	
12	
16	
11	
18	
15	
17	
13	

Fun Fruits

Count each group of fruit. Draw a line to the matching numbers.

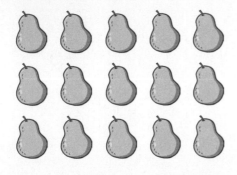

13

14

15

16

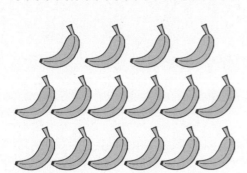

17

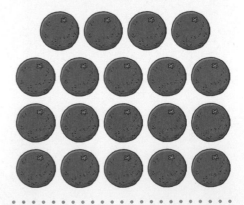

18

19

20

Flying High

Color the bows on the tails to match the number above each kite.

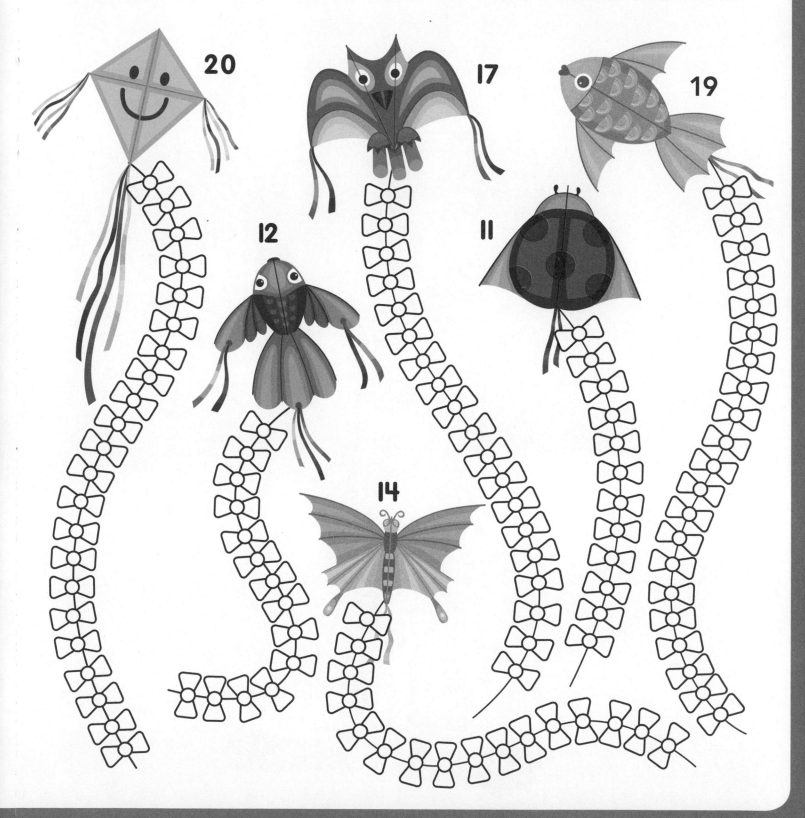

Juggling Act

Write each missing number.

Each Number in Its Spot

Write each missing number.

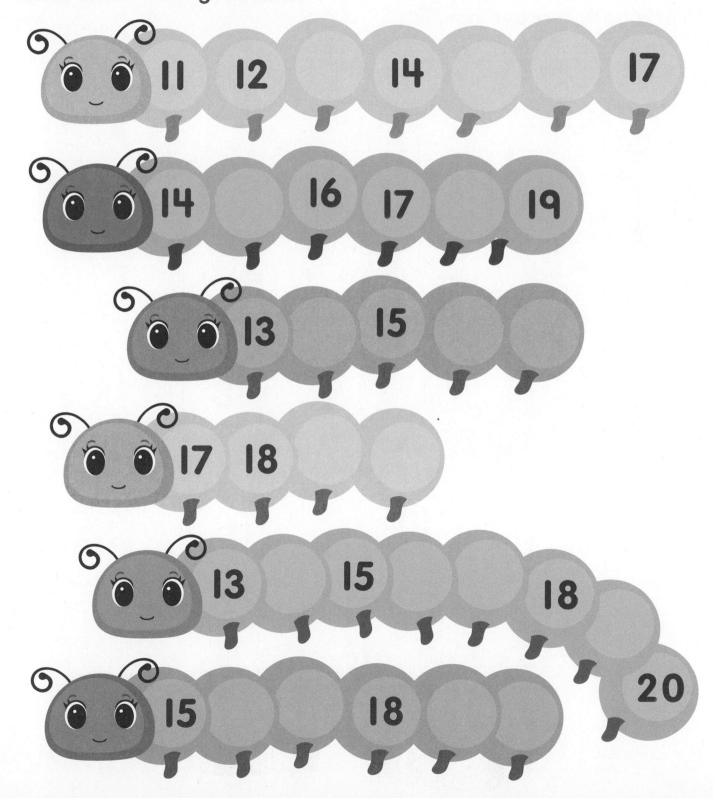

Pick Up Trash!

Help the trash collector find his way to the trash can.
Color a path in order from 1 to 20.

Start

© Scholastic Inc.

Keep on Trucking

Connect the dots from 1 to 20.

Counting Windows

Write the missing numbers.

Look-Alikes

Color the pictures with the same number as the first picture.

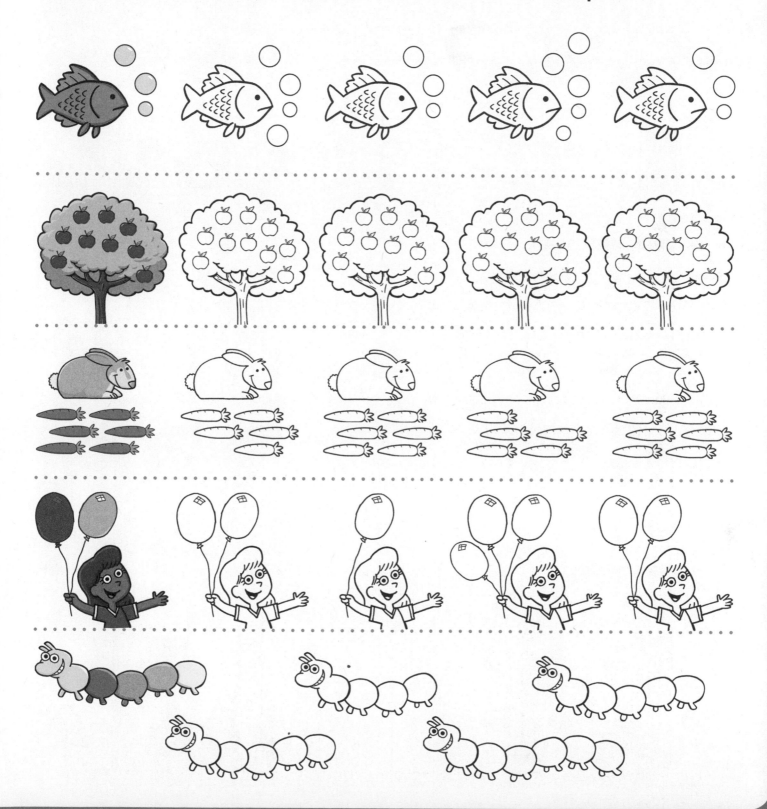

Just the Same

Draw a line to match the groups with the same number of items.

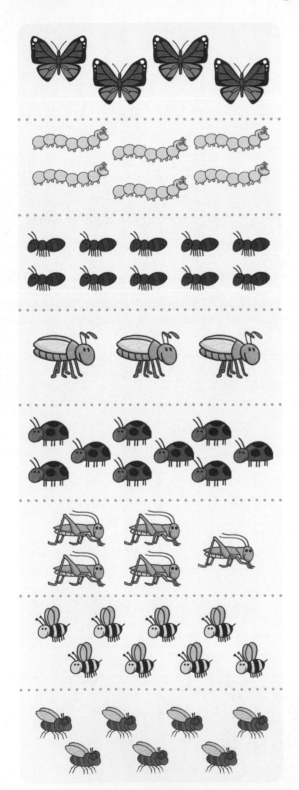
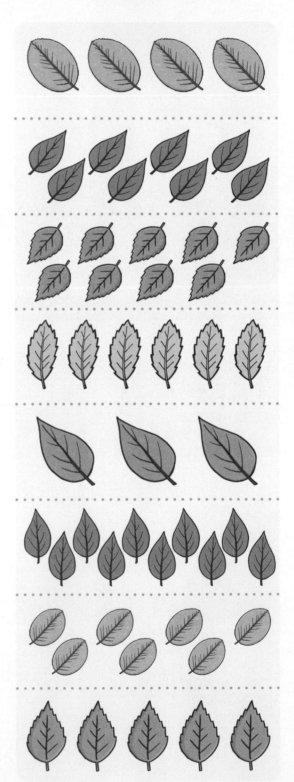

Tasty Treats

Circle the one with **more**.

A Little Snack

Circle the one with **fewer**.

Sweet Spotted Buddies

In each picture, color the dog with **more** spots.

Moving Along

Look at the picture.

Write the number. How many?

How many in all?

 and    and

 and   and

 and   and

A Perfect Day at the Park

Circle how many you see in the picture.

 1   5

 4   2

 8   5

 6   3

 7   10

 2   8

 9   7

 10   7

 3   1

Circle how many you see in all.

 + =   8   9   10

 + =   3   8   9

 + =   6   2   4

Easy as One, Two, Three

Use the color key to color the picture.

one = yellow	two = black	three = blue	four = white
five = orange	six = green	seven = red	eight = purple
nine = brown	ten = pink		

Busy Bees

Count the bees in each picture. Circle the correct number word.

twelve

fifteen

twenty

sixteen

eleven

fourteen

thirteen

nineteen

Lovely, Little Ladybugs

Count the spots on each ladybug. Circle the correct number word.

one

five

two

seven

fourteen

sixteen

nineteen

fifteen

ten

eleven

twenty

twelve

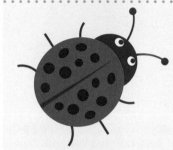
eighteen

thirteen

nine

eight

seven

four

seven

three

·SCHOLASTIC SUCCESS WITH·

HANDWRITING

Petting-Zoo Pairs

Trace the lines from each baby to its mother.

Pretty Ponies

Trace a line from each pony to its child.

A Rainy Day

Trace each line from top to bottom.

Big Balloons

Trace each line from bottom to top.

Out Comes the Sun

Trace each line from top to bottom.

Colorful Kites

Trace each line from bottom to top.

Blowing Bubbles

Trace each circle. Start at the ●. Follow the ⟶ .

Clowning Around

Trace each circle. Start at the ●. Follow the ⟶ .

Wonderful Watermelons

Trace each curved line. Start at the ●. Follow the ⟶ .

Fun at the Fair

Trace each line. Start at the ●. Follow the ⟶.

Lots of Licks

Trace and write.

Ticket Time

Trace and write.

If the weather is nice, go outside and draw straight lines on the sidewalk with large pieces of chalk.

Ooh! Aah!

Trace and write.

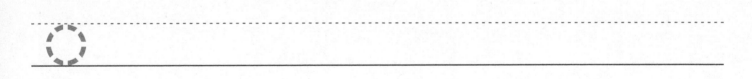

Dancing Dogs

Trace and write.

Crack! Splat!

Trace and write.

© Scholastic Inc.

Fancy Fireworks

Trace and write.

f f f f f f f

f

c c

f

Spray some shaving cream on cookie sheets. Spread out the shaving cream with your hands and use your pointer finger to draw letters in it.

Radiant Rainbow

Trace and write.

© Scholastic Inc.

Time for a Nap

Trace and write.

n n n n n n n n

n

u r

n

Go outside and practice writing letters in the sand or dirt with craft sticks.

Bouncing Balls

Trace and write.

Perfect Pumpkins

Trace and write.

P P P P P P P

p

b   h

p

Fill squeeze-type bottles with different colors of tempera paint. Squeeze the paint onto construction paper to create letters.

Jumping Goats

Trace and write.

A Quarter a Quack

Trace and write.

QUACKING DUCKS • 25¢ EACH

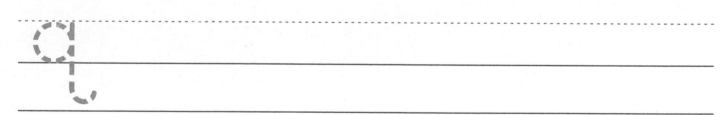

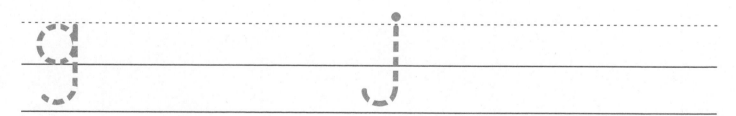

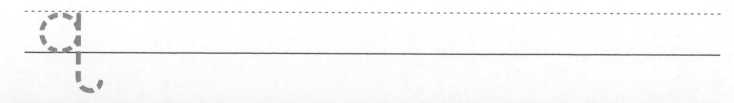

Music Makers

Trace and write.

A Vulture's Yo-Yo

Trace and write.

What Time Is It?

Trace and write.

Box Kites

Trace and write.

Zooming Along

Trace and write.

Z Z Z Z Z Z Z

Z

K X

Z

⭐ Practice forming letters using craft sticks. Glue your stick letters to construction paper.

Ice-Cold Lemonade

Trace and write.

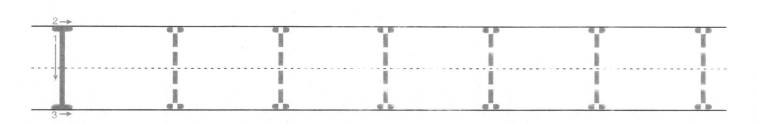

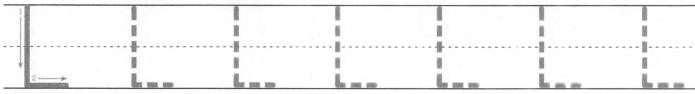

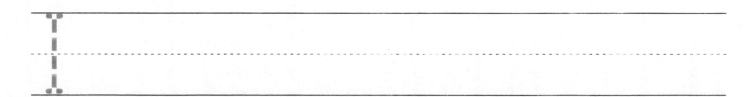

Toot-Toot!

Trace and write.

Making Friends at the Fair

Trace and write.

Hungry for Hot Dogs

Trace and write.

© Scholastic Inc.

A Cozy Quilt

Trace and write.

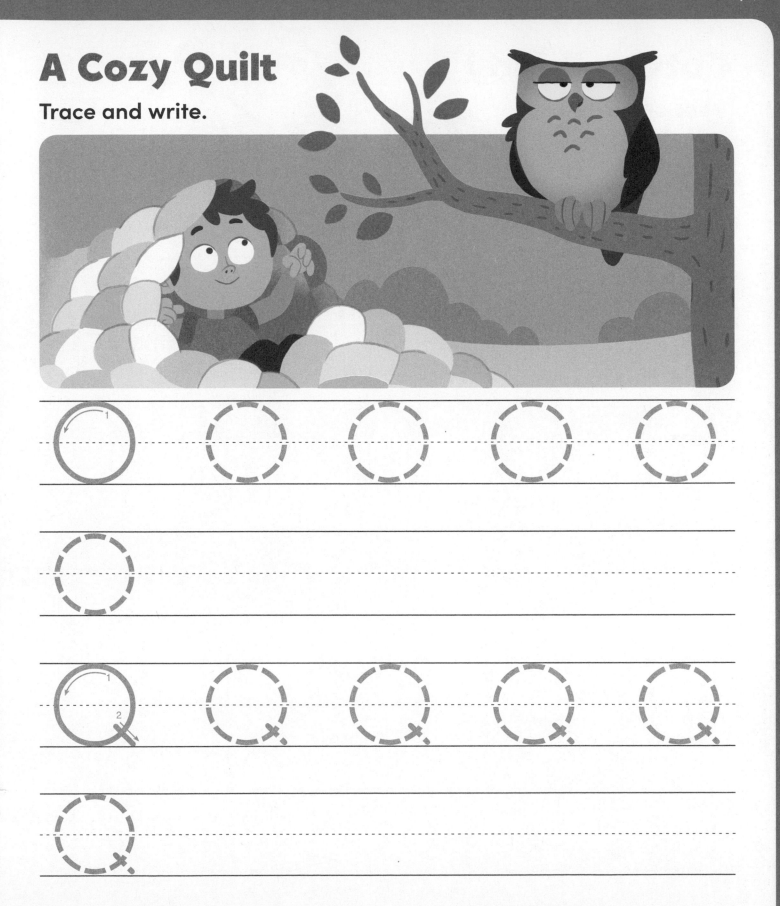

Cotton Candy

Trace and write.

© Scholastic Inc.

The Dunking Booth

Trace and write.

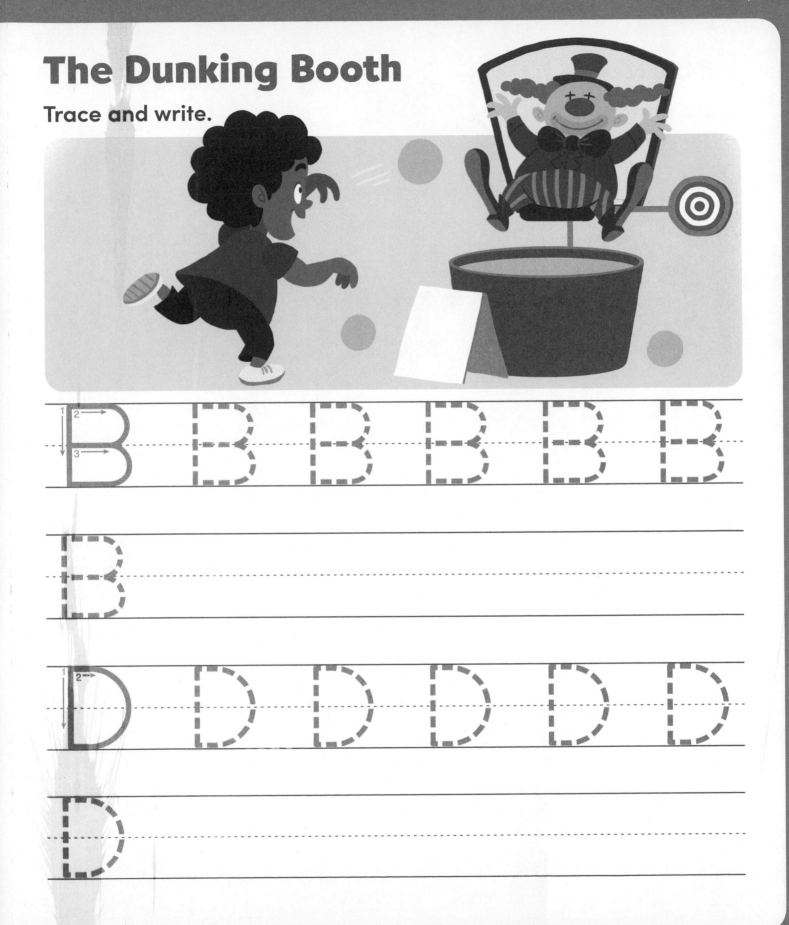

Feeding Time

Trace and write.

Rolling Roller Coaster

Trace and write.

P P P P P P P P

P

R R R R R R R R

R

Up, Up, and Away!

Trace and write.

Scholastic Success With Kindergarten

Sack-Jumping

Trace and write.

J J J J J J

J

S S S S S S

S

Ant Antics

Trace and write.

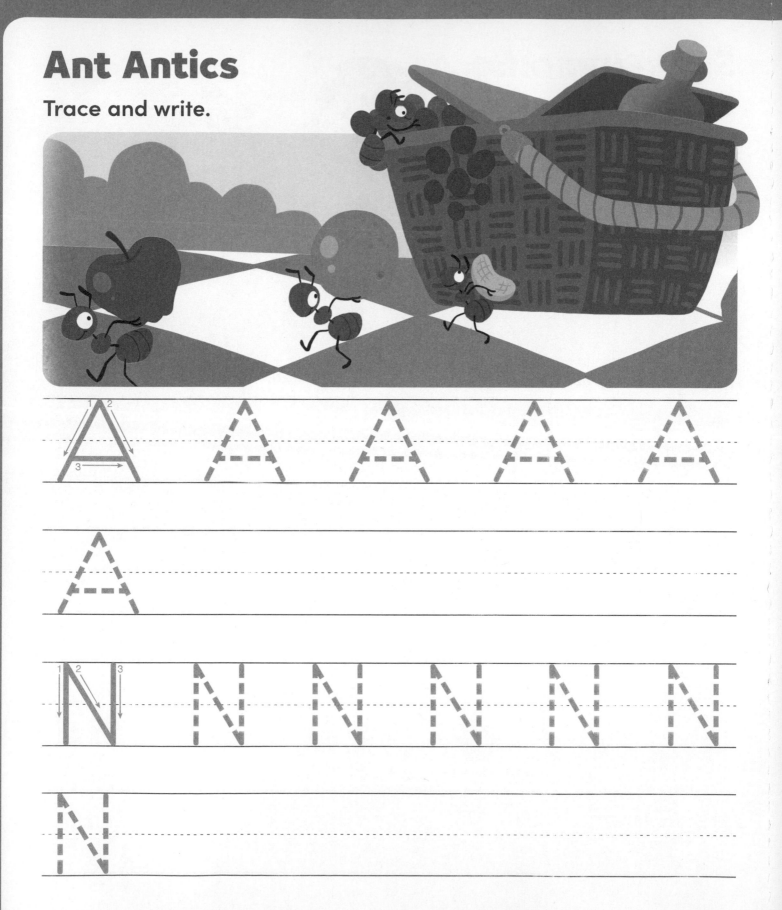

Merrily We Go Around!

Trace and write.

What a Day!

Trace and write.

A Youthful Yawn

Trace and write.

Can We Keep One?

Trace and write.

The Petting Zoo

Trace and write.

A–Z

Trace and write.

A B C D E F G H I

J K L M N O P Q

R S T U V W X Y Z

a–z

Trace and write.

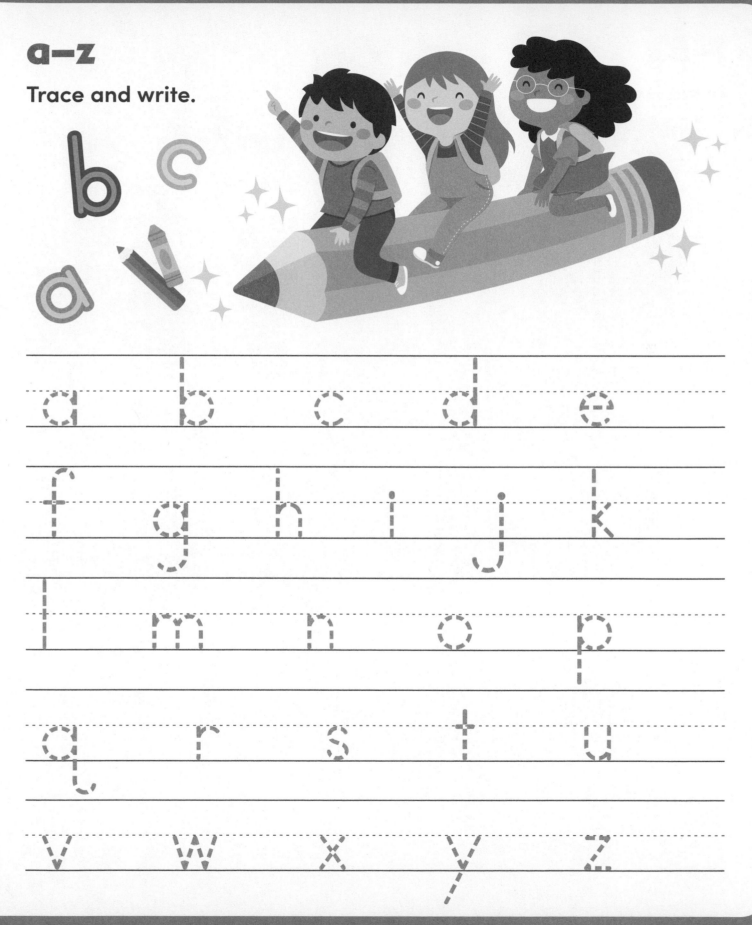

a b c d e

f g h i j k

l m n o p

q r s t u

v w x y z

1–5

Trace and write.

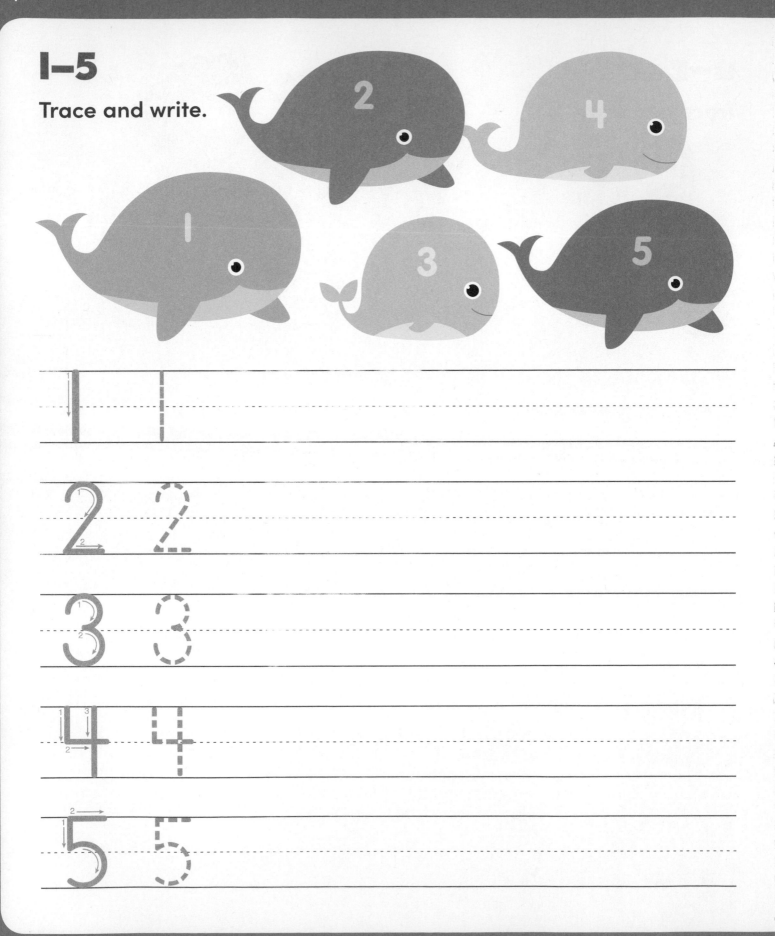

6–10

Trace and write.

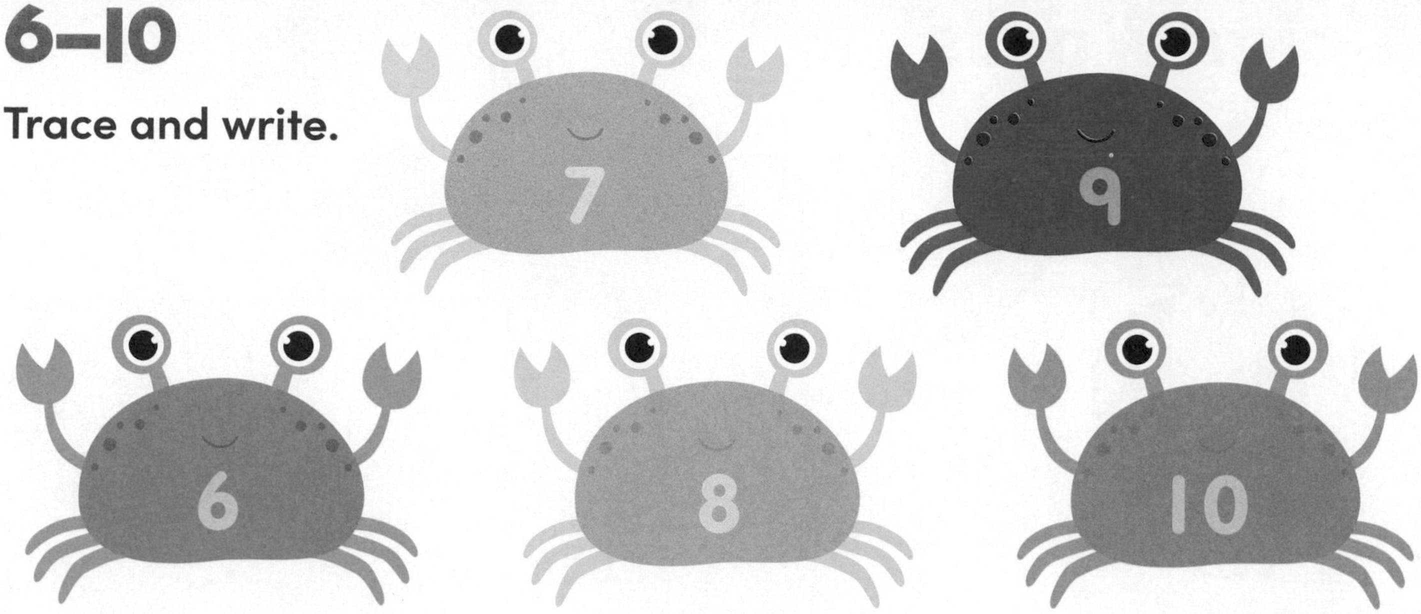

6 6

7 7

8 8

9 9

10 10

Color Words

Trace and write.

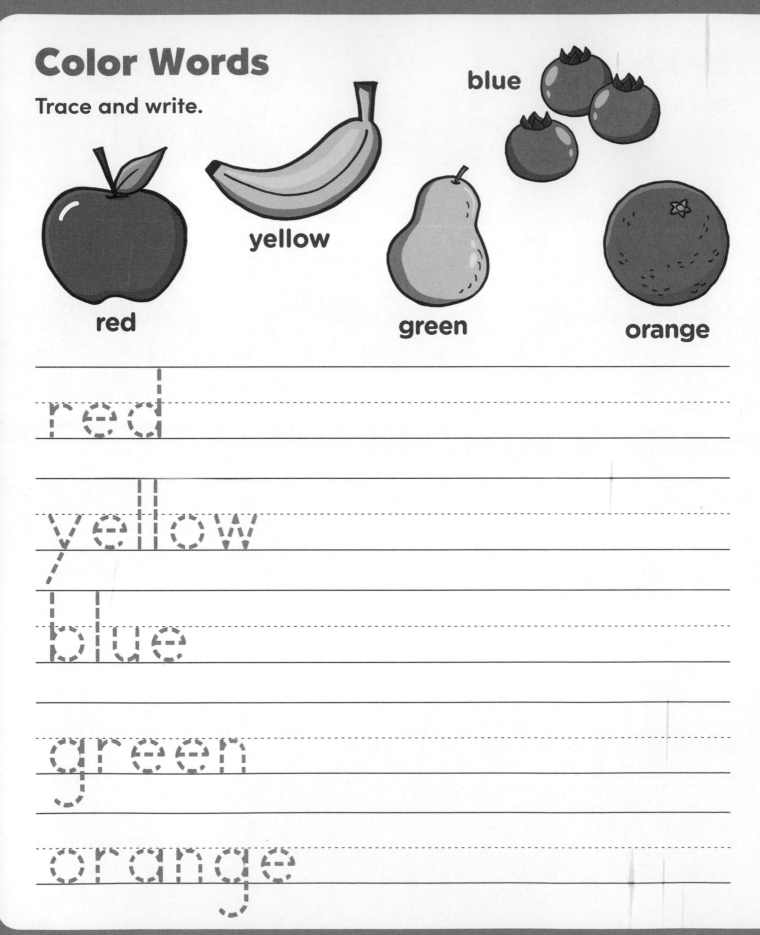

red

yellow

blue

green

orange

red

yellow

blue

green

orange

More Color Words

Trace and write.

black

purple

brown

white

pink

purple

brown

black

white

pink

Number Words

Trace and write.

one

two

three

four

five

1 one

2 two

3 three

4 four

5 five

More Number Words

Trace and write.

six

seven

eight

nine

ten

6 six

7 seven

8 eight

9 nine

10 ten

Shapes

Trace and write.

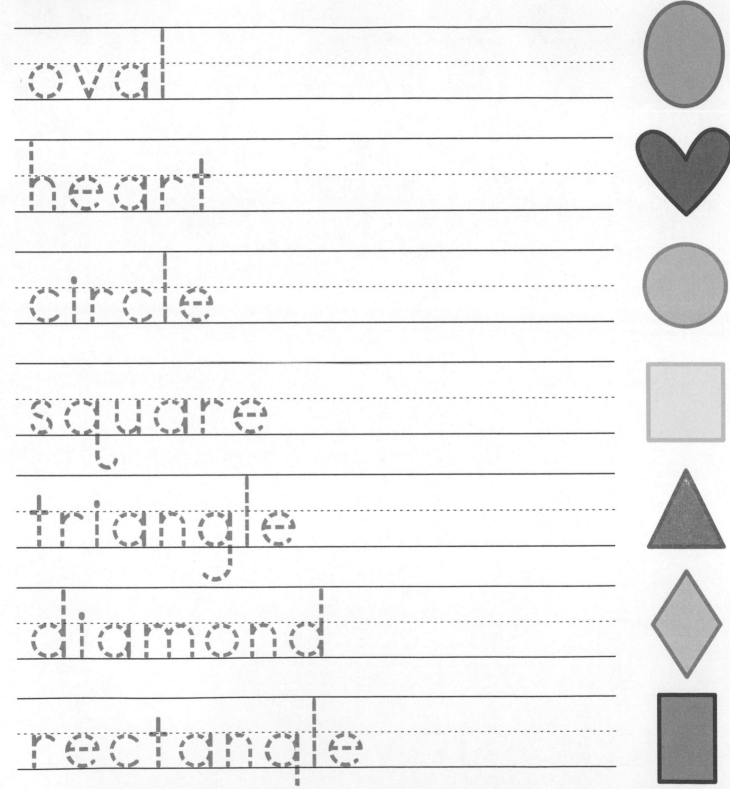

oval

heart

circle

square

triangle

diamond

rectangle

Days of the Week

Trace and write.

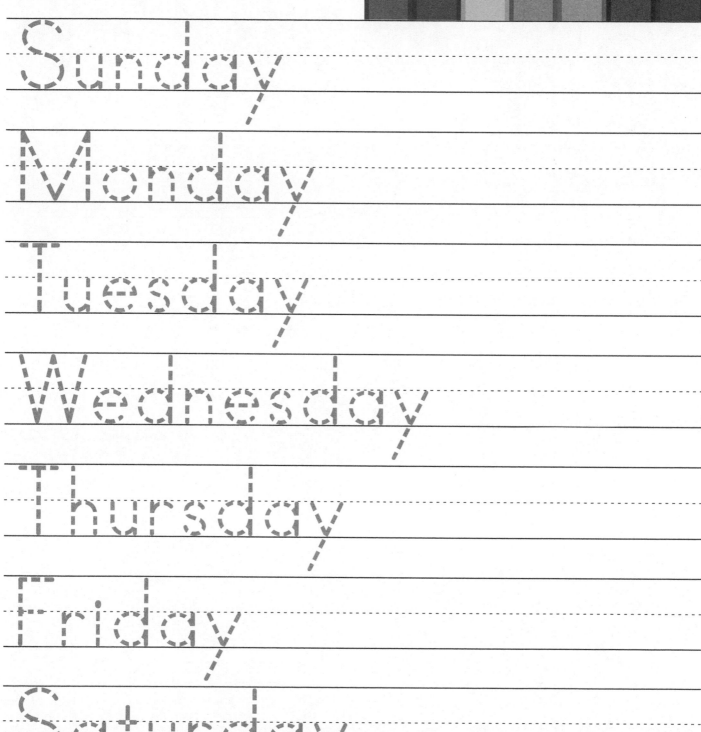

Sunday

Monday

Tuesday

Wednesday

Thursday

Friday

Saturday

Months

Trace and write.

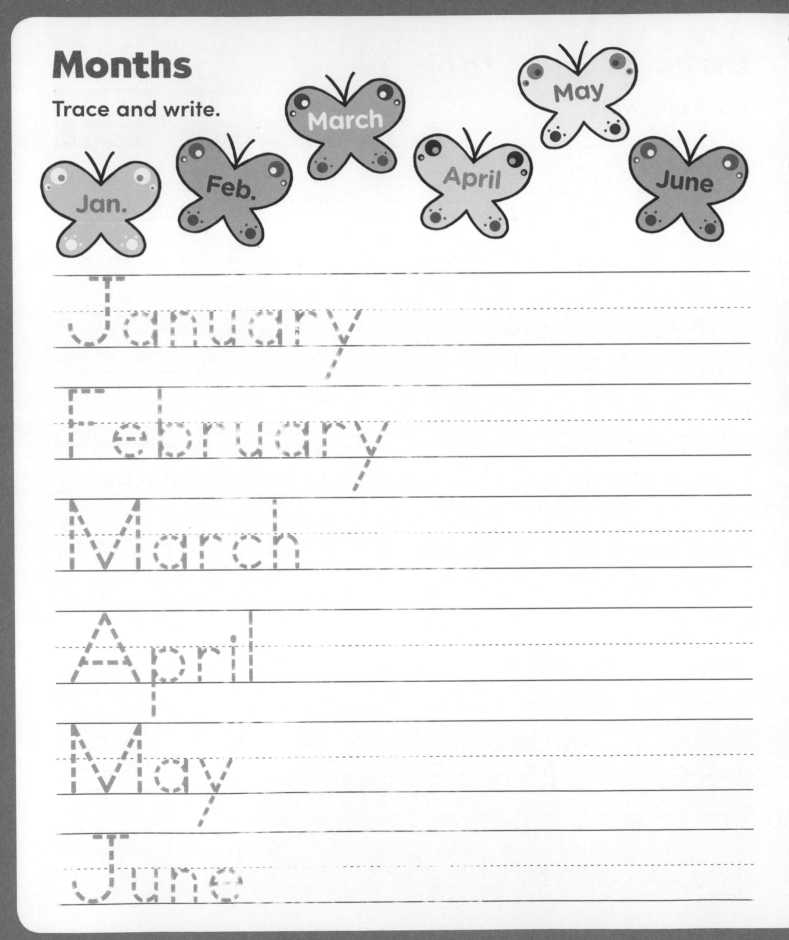

January

February

March

April

May

June

Months

Trace and write.

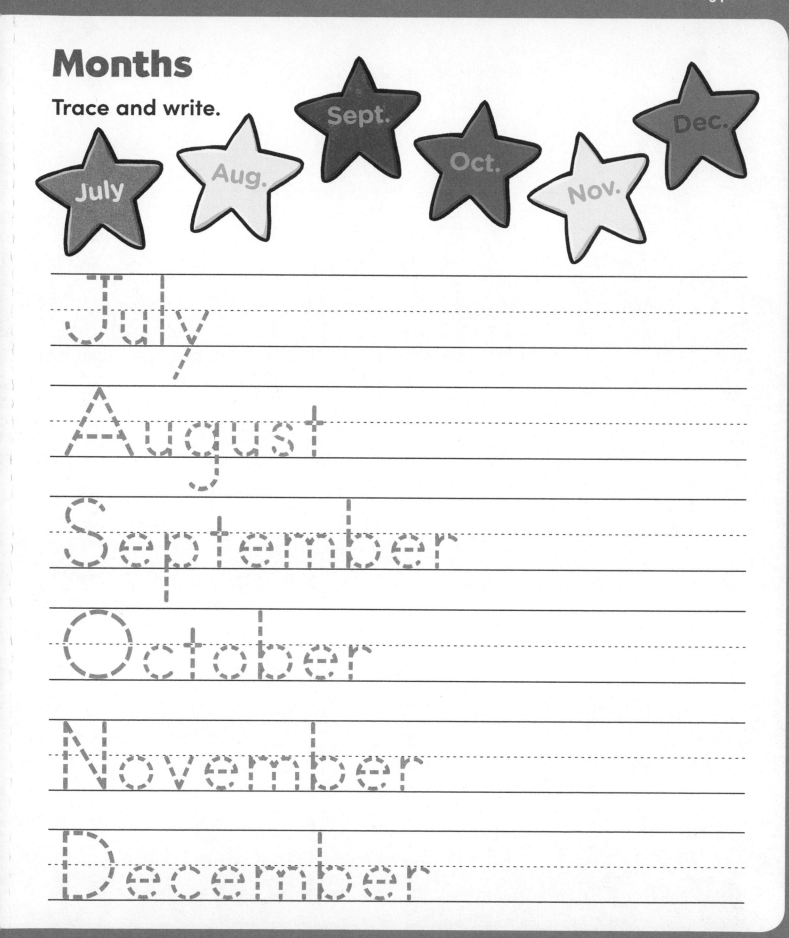

July

August

September

October

November

December

Practice writing words.

_____

- - - - - - - - - - - - - - - - - -

_____

- - - - - - - - - - - - - - - - - -

_____

- - - - - - - - - - - - - - - - - -

_____

- - - - - - - - - - - - - - - - - -

_____

- - - - - - - - - - - - - - - - - -

_____

BASIC CONCEPTS

Coloring Crayons

Color each crayon to show its color.
Draw a line from each crayon to its matching color word.

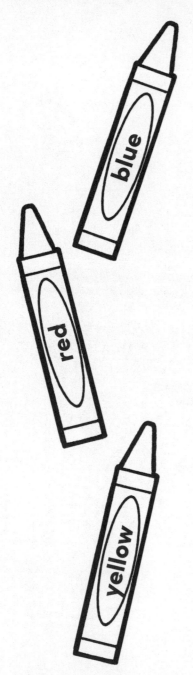

red

yellow

orange

blue

green

purple

 Name three things that are red.

What Color Am I?

Say the color words. Color the pictures.

yellow

red

green

black

orange

brown

blue

purple

 On another sheet of paper, draw four things that are green.

Color Train

Draw a line to match each picture to the correct color. Color.

Rolling Through the Hills

Color the picture.

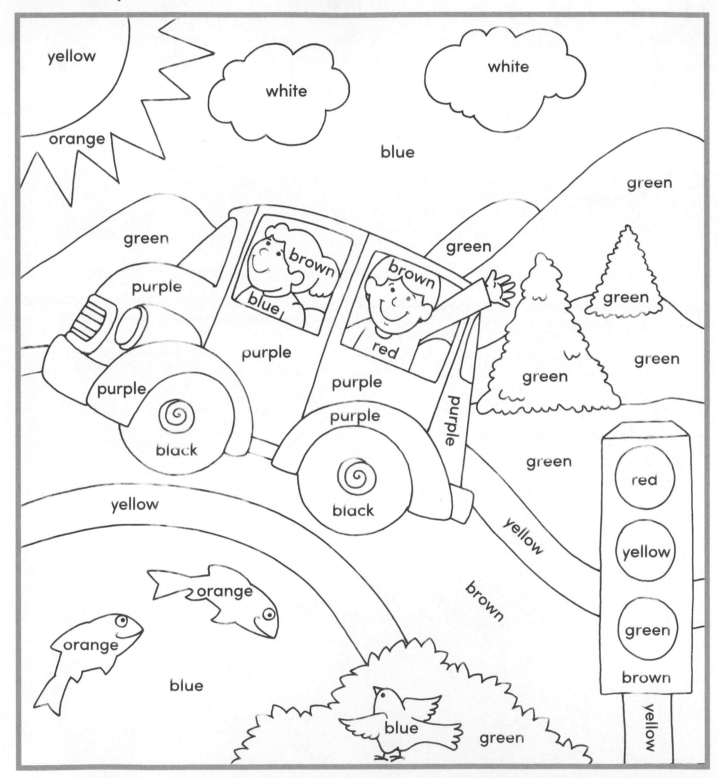

Sorting Shapes

This is a **circle** ◯. This is a **square** ☐.
A square has four sides that are the same length.
This is a **rectangle** ▭. A rectangle also has four sides.
The opposite sides of a rectangle are the same length.
This is a **triangle** △. A triangle has three sides.

Color the circles ◯ yellow. Color the squares ▪ red.
Color the triangles ▲ green. Color the rectangles ▬ blue.

Circle and Square Search

Color each circle shape.

Color each square shape.

Rectangle and Triangle Teasers

Color each rectangle shape.

Color each triangle shape.

Oval and Diamond Detectives

Color each diamond shape.

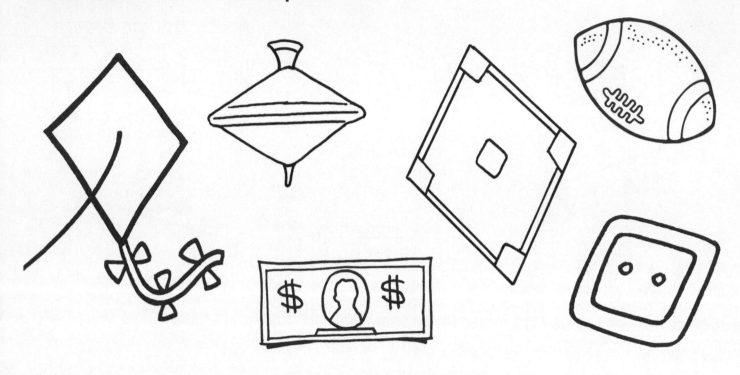

Color each oval shape.

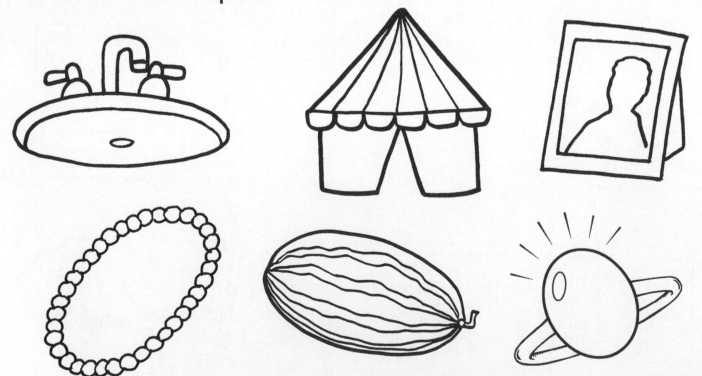

Shape Match-Up

Trace each shape. Draw a line to match each object to its shape. Color.

triangle

square

circle

rectangle

More Shape Match-Up

Trace each shape. Draw a line to match each object to its shape. Color.

square

oval

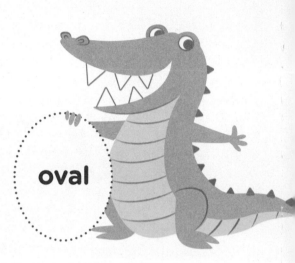

diamond

rectangle

Shape Teasers

Color each shape. Use the color key.

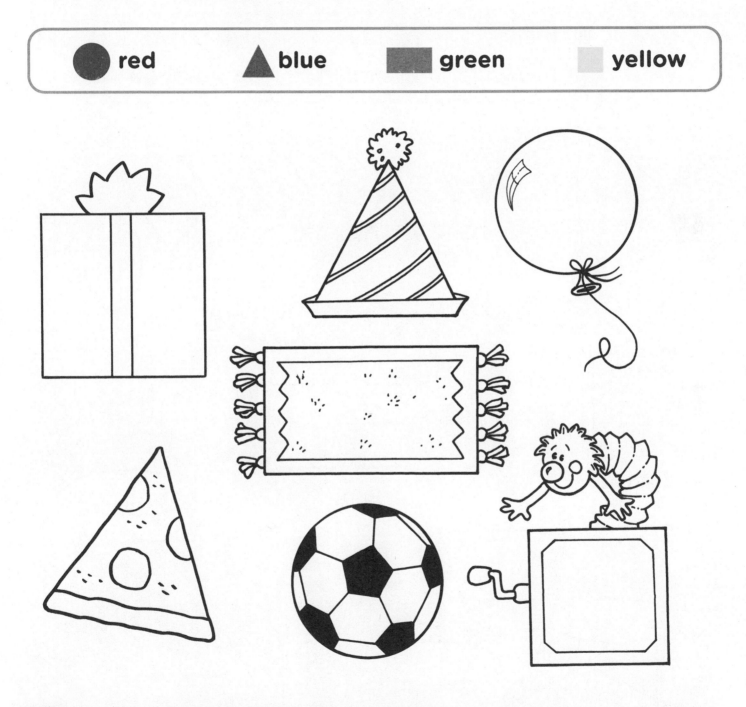

⭐ Name something else with each shape.

Zany Shapes

Color each shape in the picture. Use the color key.

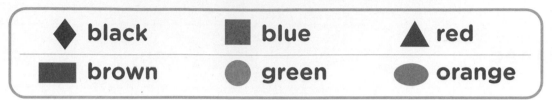

◆ black	■ blue	▲ red
▬ brown	● green	⬭ orange

Flying High With Shapes

Color each shape in the picture. Use the color key.

◆ purple	▢ yellow	▲ orange
▭ green	● blue	⬭ red

A Shapely Castle

Color each shape in the picture. Use the color key.

Smiling Shapes

What shape is next in each pattern? Draw a line to match it.

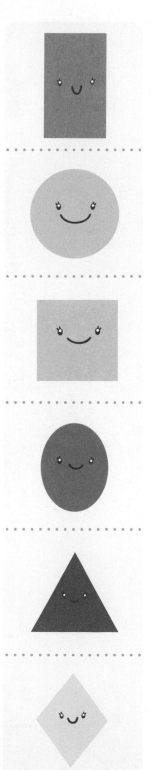

What Comes Next?

What shape is next in each pattern? Circle it.

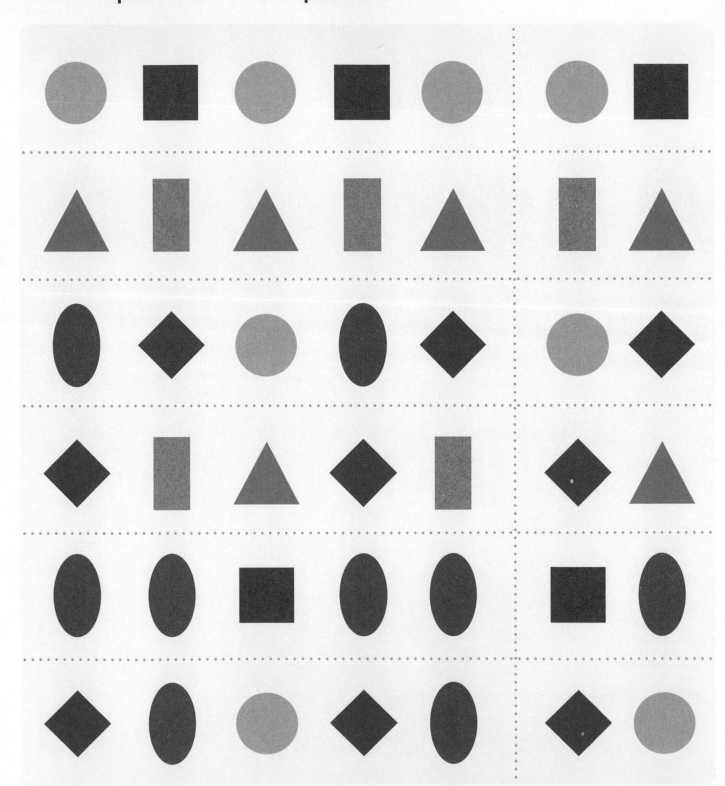

Ordering Outfits

What shape is next in each pattern? Circle it.

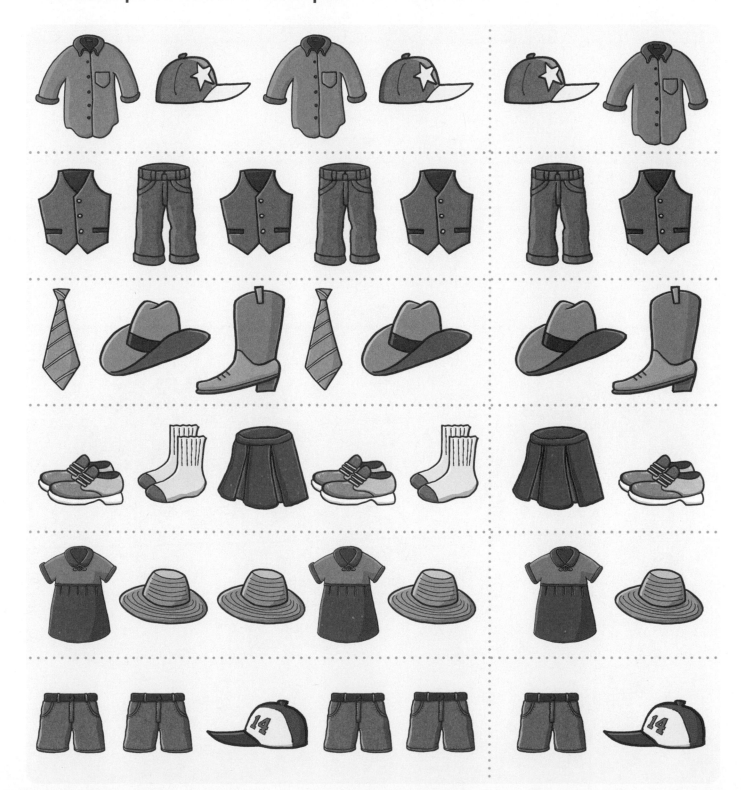

Decorate a Headband

Draw shapes to finish each pattern. Then color the headbands.

You Can Draw an Apple!

1 Draw a circle with two bumps on top.	2 Draw a rectangle for the stem.	3 Draw a pointed leaf.

You Can Draw a Balloon!

1 Draw an oval.

2 Draw a small triangle on the bottom.

3 Add a curved line for the string.

You Can Draw a Kite!

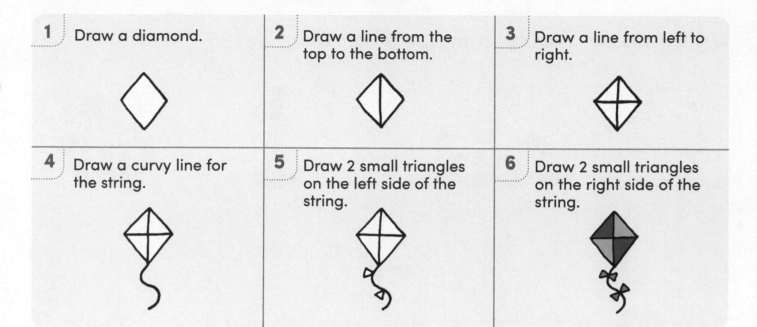

1 Draw a diamond.

2 Draw a line from the top to the bottom.

3 Draw a line from left to right.

4 Draw a curvy line for the string.

5 Draw 2 small triangles on the left side of the string.

6 Draw 2 small triangles on the right side of the string.

Everything in Order

Write 1 under what happens first.
Write 2 under what happens second.

 Think about this: What do you do first when you wake up?

First Things First

Write **1** under what happens first.

Write **2** under what happens next.

Write **3** under what happens last.

Perfect Order

**What happens first, next, and last?
Write 1, 2, and 3 to show the order.**

Out of Place

Name each item in the pictures. Circle two things in each picture that do not belong. Color the pictures.

Where Do I Belong?

Draw a line to show where each thing belongs.

 On another sheet of paper, draw a picture of something that might be on a farm.

Going to School

Find and color these things in the picture.

pencil paper glue book scissors eraser

 Circle one thing in the picture that does not belong.

Up, Down, and All Around

This mouse is **up**.   This mouse is **down**.

Color the animals that are up red.
Color the animals that are down blue.

 Count the animals. Write the number. Up _____ Down _____

Pretty Balloons

This is **low**. | This is **high**.

Color the balloons that are low yellow.
Color the balloons that are high purple.

Up on Top

Draw a ◯ around the at the **top**.

Draw a ◯ around the at the **top**.

Draw a ◯ around the at the **bottom**.

Draw a ◯ around the at the **bottom**.

Above or Below... Sure You Know!

Draw a ☐ around the 🐝 **above** the 🌸.

Draw a ☐ around the 🐞 **above** the 🍃.

Draw a ☐ around the 🐰 **below** the 🎩.

Draw a ☐ around the 🐕 **below** the ⬜.

Quacky Business

This duck is **over**.   This duck is **under**.

Circle the correct answer.

1 **Where do you see more ducks?**   over   under

2 **Where do you see more frogs?**   over   under

In, Out, and All About

This animal is **in**. | This animal is **out**.

Color each animal that is in its home.

More In, Out, and All About

Color the animals that are **in** their homes.

Size It Up

Draw a ◇ around the picture that is **short**.

Draw a ◇ around the picture that is **long**.

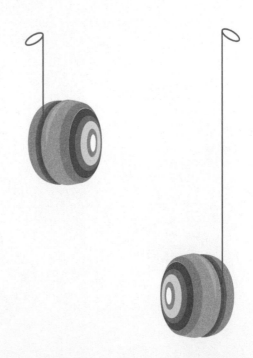

Transportation Station

Draw a ☐ around the picture that is **big**.

Draw a ☐ around the picture that is **small**.

Just the Right Size

This butterfly is **large**. : This butterfly is **small**.

Circle the large item on each petal.

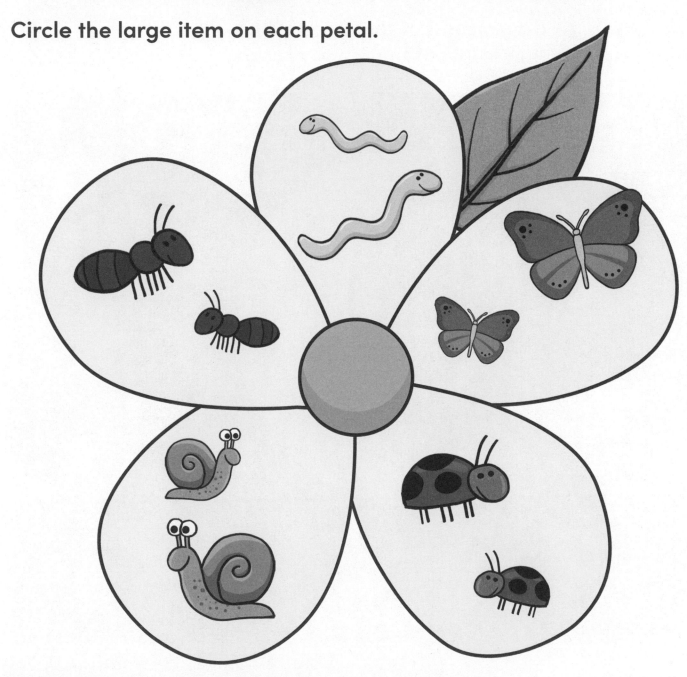

 Name two things that are larger than you.

Star Lights

The star is **right** of the moon.   The star is **left** of the moon.

Color each ⭐ that is right of the moon yellow.
Color each ⭐ that is left of the moon orange.

 How many stars do you see in all?

Mark the Map

Trace a **LEFT** or **RIGHT** path in each picture.

How Do You Feel?

Sometimes you feel **happy**. : Sometimes you feel **sad**.

Look at each picture. Draw a line to the happy or sad face to show how each picture makes you feel.

Tricks or Treats

Count. In each row, circle the dog with **fewer** treats.

Time for a Picnic

The gray rabbit has **more** carrots.
The brown rabbit has **fewer** carrots.

Write how many. Circle the group that has more.

_____   _____   _____   _____   _____   _____

Write how many. Circle the group that has fewer.

_____   _____   _____   _____   _____   _____

What Is Really Real?

Color the real pictures. Do not color the pretend pictures.

Things that are **pretend** are not **real**.

 Make up a story about a pretend trip to the moon. Tell your story to a grown-up.

A Silly City

Circle 5 pretend things in the picture.

Searching for Opposites

An elephant is **big** . A mouse is **little** . *Big* and *little* are **opposites**.

Circle the picture that shows the opposite.

happy · · · sad

up · · · down

wet · · · dry

fast · · · slow

 Name something you can do fast. Name something you can do slowly.

Searching for More Opposites

Circle the picture that shows the opposite.

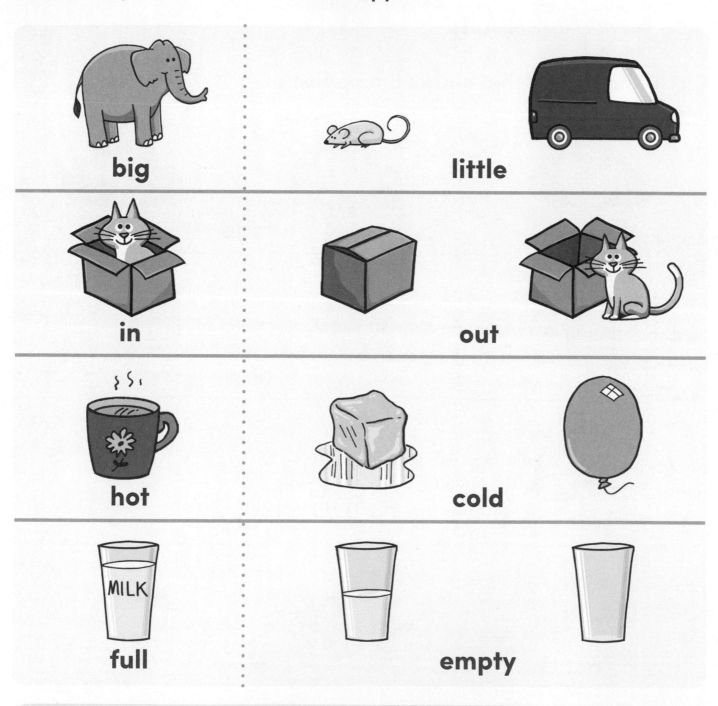

big   little

in   out

hot   cold

full   empty

 On another sheet of paper, draw a picture of something that might be larger than an elephant.

Different as Can Be

Follow the maze to match the pictures that show the opposite.

A Perfect Match

  and are the **same**.

Draw a line to connect the cars that are the same.

 Name one way you and a friend are the same.

A Ride in the Clouds

 and are **different**.

Circle the plane that is different in each row.

 Name one way you and a friend are different.

Triangle Teasers

Draw a △ around the picture that is different.

Small but Strong

This bug is **small**.	This bug is **smaller**.	This bug is **smallest**.

Put an X on the smallest animal in each row.

 On another sheet of paper, draw something smaller than a watermelon.

Bigger and Better

This bear is **big**.	This bear is **bigger**.	This bear is **biggest**.

Draw a ▭ around the biggest animal in each row.

 On another sheet of paper, draw a picture of something bigger than a bear.

Side by Side

Draw a line to match the pictures that go together.

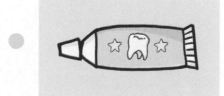

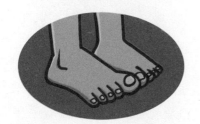

Out of Place

In each set, put an **X** on the picture that does not belong.

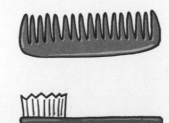

Together Is Better

Color the picture that goes with the first picture in each row.

	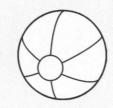	

		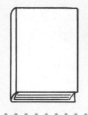

Special Helpers

Draw a line to match the workers to their tools.

I Want My Mommy!

Draw a line from each each mother to its baby.

 Circle the baby that hatches from an egg.

How Is the Weather?

Draw a line from each type of weather to an activity you could do.

What we can do outside each day depends on the weather.

sunny

windy

snowy

rainy

All Dressed Up

Connect the top, bottom, and shoes that go together.

We wear **clothes** to go with the weather.

 What do you like to wear? On another sheet of paper, draw a picture of you in your favorite clothes.

Community Helpers

Draw a line to match each worker to something he or she uses to help others.

 Think of three things you can do to help your family.

© Scholastic Inc.

Time to Work

Color the tool in each row that the worker needs.

 Talk about what you want to be when you grow up.

Time to Travel

Color the transportation for land **green**.
Color the transportation for water **blue**.
Color the transportation for air **purple**.

Transportation is how we get from one place to another.

 Name all the kinds of transportation you have used.

Totally Amazing!

Draw a line to each body part.

The **body** is made up of many parts.

eyes

. . . .

hair

. . . .

nose

. . . .

leg

. . . .

arm

. . . .

foot

. . . .

hand

. . . .

chest

 Name three other body parts.

Sensational Senses

We use our **senses** to learn about new things.

We **see** with our	We **hear** with our	We **smell** with our	We **taste** with our	We **touch** with our

Look at each picture. Circle the sense you would use.

					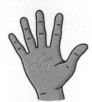

A Place to Call Home

Find the children's houses on the map. Then use the color words on their shirts to color the houses.

I live at 25 Oak Lane.

blue

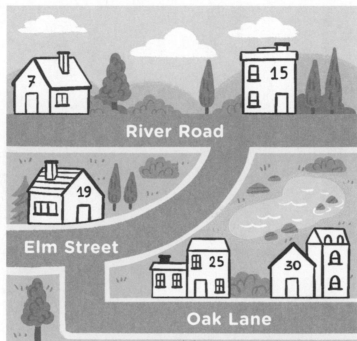

River Road

Elm Street

Oak Lane

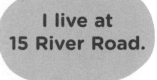

I live at 15 River Road.

red

I live at 30 Oak Lane.

yellow

I live at 19 Elm Street.

green

I live at 7 River Road.

purple

Where do you live? Say your address.

All in the Family

Write the names of each member of your family.
Sort them into the correct categories.

Adults	Children

SCHOLASTIC SUCCESS WITH

PHONICS

Hop to It!

In each row, color the lily pad with the letter that matches the frog. Then, circle the picture that begins with that letter.

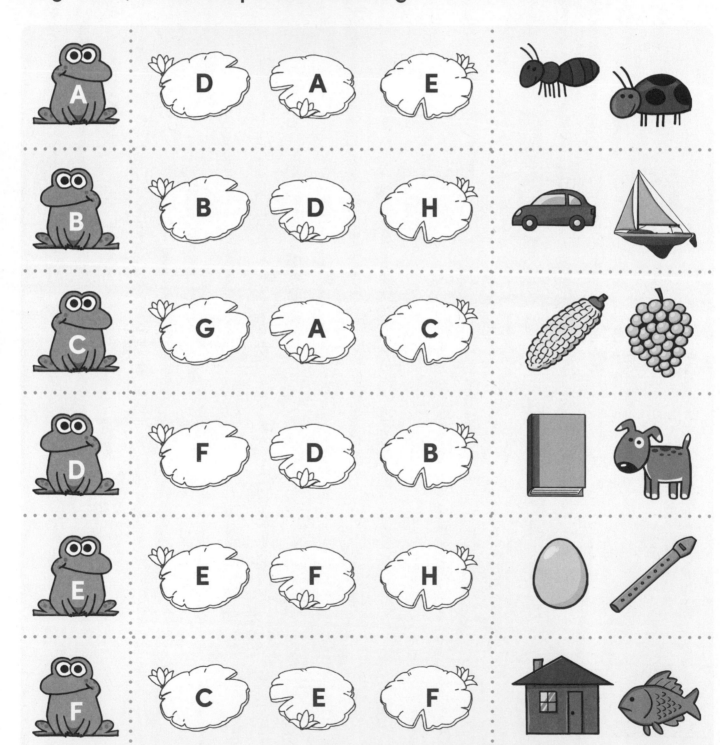

In each row, color the lily pad with the letter that matches the frog. Then, circle the picture that begins with that letter.

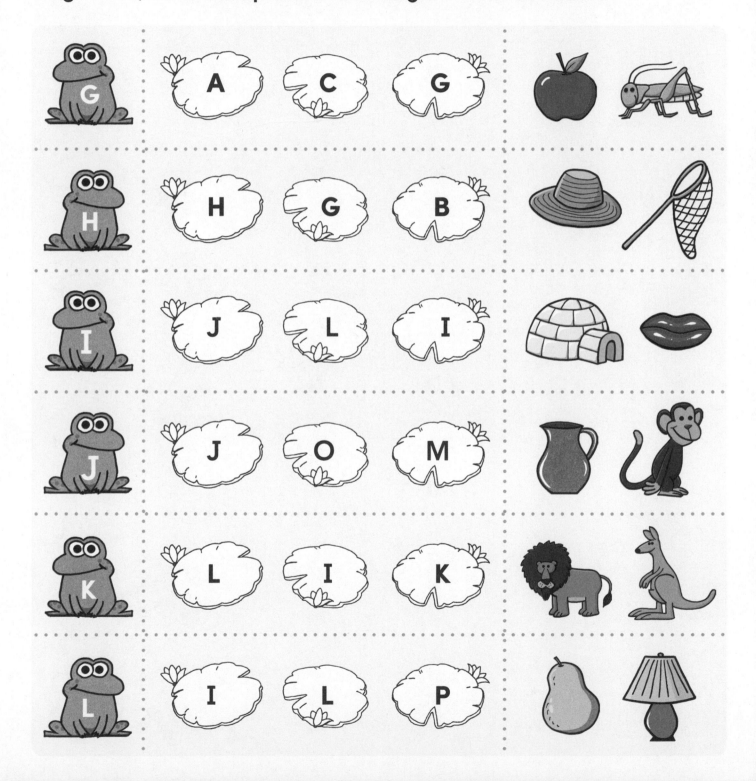

Letter Flags

In each row, color the carrot with the letter that matches the flag.
Then, circle the picture that begins with that letter.

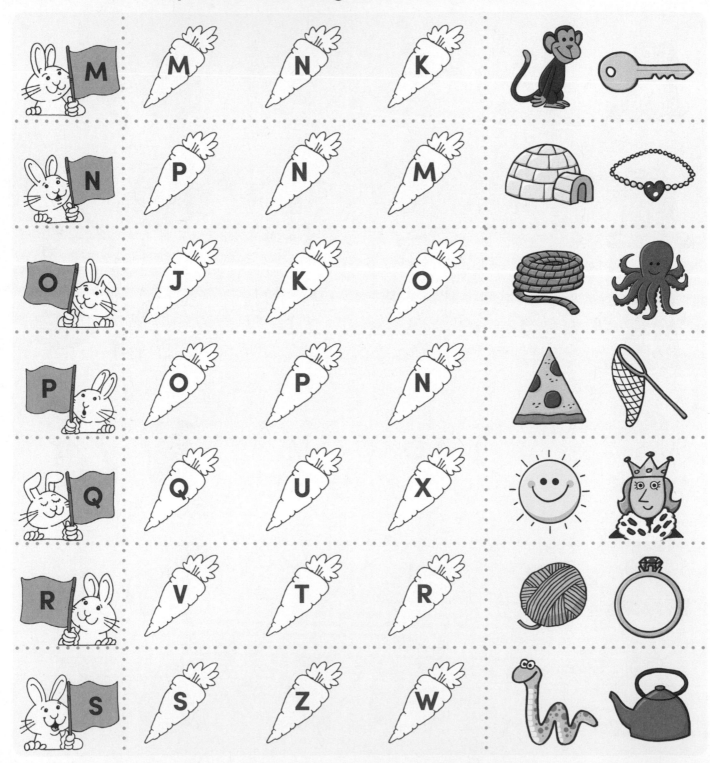

In each row, color the carrot with the letter that matches the flag.
Then, circle the picture that begins with that letter.

What Is a Consonant?

Look at the alphabet below. Mark an **X** through the five vowels: *A, E, I, O,* and *U.* Now say the names of all the consonants.

There are 26 letters in the alphabet. Five of the letters are vowels: *A, E, I, O,* and *U.* All the rest are consonants.

A B C D E F G H I
J K L M N O P Q
R S T U V W X Y Z

How many consonants are there? _____

Color each balloon that has a consonant in it.

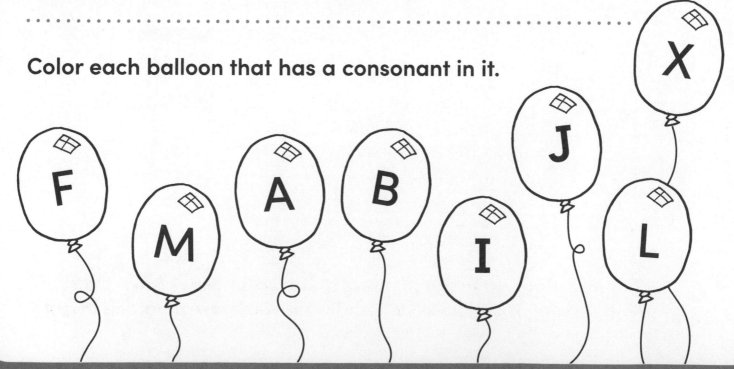

Bobby the Bear

Bobby the bear is going shopping for things that begin with **b**. Help Bobby find five things in this store that begin with **b**. Draw a circle around each one.

B makes the sound you hear at the beginning of the words *Bobby* and *bear*.

 What insect buzzes around flowers and makes honey? Draw it on another sheet of paper. Tell a friend what you know about this insect.

Doctor Dave

Look in Doctor Dave's bag. Color only the pictures that begin with **d**. Put an **X** on the pictures that do not begin with **d**.

D makes the sound you hear at the beginning of the words *doctor* and *Dave*.

 What kind of doctor works on your teeth? The name begins with *d*. On another sheet of paper, draw yourself at the doctor's office.

Fancy the Fish

Fancy the fish is blowing bubbles. Draw a bubble around the pictures that begin with **f**. Put an **X** on the pictures that do not begin with **f**.

F makes the sound you hear at the beginning of the words *fancy* and *fish*.

 What brave person saves people when their houses are burning? On another sheet of paper, draw a picture of this person's truck.

Happy the Hippo

Help Happy the hippo find the **h** words. Say the picture in each box. Color only the pictures that begin with **h**.

H makes the sound you hear at the beginning of the words *happy* and *hippo*.

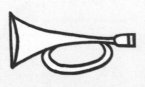   

 This game begins with *h*. One child counts to ten and then tries to find the other children. What game is it?

Joe the Janitor

Help Joe the janitor find the j words. Draw a box around the pictures that begin with j.

J makes the sound you hear at the beginning of the words *Joe* and *janitor*.

 What kind of candy begins with *j*, looks like beans, and comes in lots of different colors? Say the answer.

Katie the Kangaroo

Help Katie the kangaroo find the pictures that begin with **k**. Color them in.

K makes the sound you hear at the beginning of the words *Katie* and *kangaroo*.

 This word begins with *k*. It can mean a young goat, or it can mean a young person. It rhymes with *lid*. What is it?

Lazy the Lion

Help Lazy the lion find a word that begins with **l** to match each picture. Circle the correct word.

L makes the sound you hear at the beginning of the words *lazy* and *lion*.

lamp   clock

zipper   lace

tree   leaf

ladder   hoe

ladybug   bee

lake   town

dog   lamb

hand   leg

lightning   snow

apple   lemon

book   letter

lettuce   corn

nose   lips

lizard   goat

worm   lobster

log   rock

This word begins with an *l*. It is a good feeling that you have about the people you like the most. What is it?

Marci the Mail Carrier

Help Marci the mail carrier sort the mail. Find the pieces of mail that have a picture that begins with **m**. Draw a line from the picture to the bag marked with an **m**.

M makes the sound you hear at the beginning of the words *Marci* and *mail*.

Nancy the Nurse

After Nancy the nurse gives a shot, she also gives a lollipop to help her young patients feel better. Color the lollipops below that have pictures beginning with **n**.

N makes the sound you hear at the beginning of the words *Nancy* and *nurse*.

Patsy the Pig

Help Patsy the pig find the words that begin with **p**. Use a purple crayon to write the letter **p** on top of each picture below that begins with **p**.

P makes the sound you hear at the beginning of the words *Patsy* and *pig*.

⭐ This item begins with *p*. It has a head and a tail, but it is not an animal. It is a copper-colored coin. What is it?

Ricky the Rabbit

Look at all the fun things that Ricky the rabbit can do. Circle the **r** word that tells what Ricky is doing in each picture.

R makes the sound you hear at the beginning of the words *Ricky* and *rabbit*.

rest   play

swim   run

ride   hug

rock   look

climb   rake

stand   roll

read   sing

rope   feed

rip   talk

row   eat

race   walk

sleep   rush

 This word begins with *r*. It blasts off into outer space. It orbits Earth. What is it?

Silly Sally

Silly Sally is looking for something that starts with **s**. Help her find it in the puzzle below. Color each space that has a picture in it that begins with **s** orange. If the picture does not begin with **s**, do not color that space.

S makes the sound you hear at the beginning of the words *silly* and *Sally*.

 If you take two pieces of bread and put peanut butter on one and jelly on the other, then stick them together, what have you made?

Tammy the Teacher

Trace the letter in each row. Color the pictures in each row that begin with t.

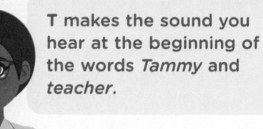

T makes the sound you hear at the beginning of the words *Tammy* and *teacher*.

 This item begins with *t*. Campers sleep in it. What is it?

Vicki's Vacation

Vicki is going on a vacation. Help Vicki load her van with things that start with **v**. Draw a line from the **v** words to the van.

V makes the sound you hear at the beginning of the words *Vicki* and *vacation*.

 What kind of mountain has lava inside? Sometimes the lava comes out of the top and runs down the sides. **Hint:** It begins with the letter *v*. On another sheet of paper, draw one and color it.

Willy the Worm

In the story below, there are 11 words that begin with w. Draw a wiggly line under each one.

W makes the sound you hear at the beginning of the words *Willy* and *worm*.

Willy the worm felt hungry. He
wanted something to eat. He saw
a watermelon in the window.
He climbed onto the wagon.
He wiggled up the wall. Then he
took a bite. Wow! It was wonderful!

Now, circle each word that you underlined in the puzzle. The words go across and down.

```
x w i g g l e d v t
w a t e r m e l o n
o g e k p r s b y w
w o r m h f l x z i
k n c w i n d o w l
g v w a n t e d a l
u w h s r z q g l y
w o n d e r f u l a
```

This begins with *w*. You cannot see it, but you can feel it. Sometimes you can hear it blowing. It makes the trees sway. What is it?

Yolanda's Yearbook

Yolanda got a yearbook at school today. It has funny pictures in it. Which pictures go together? Draw lines to match the pictures in Yolanda's yearbook. The words in each picture begin with y. Can you say them?

Y makes the sound you hear at the beginning of the words *Yolanda* and *yearbook*.

© Scholastic Inc.

Zachary the Zebra

Zachary the zebra is lost! Help him find his way back to the zoo. Circle only the things that begin with **z**. Connect them to the **z**'s you find along the way.

Z makes the sound you hear at the beginning of the words *Zachary* and *zebra*.

 What word begins with *z* and sounds like a car speeding by very fast? **Hint:** It rhymes with *broom*. On another sheet of paper, draw a race car. Think of a story to tell with your picture.

Hidden Picture

Say the pictures in the puzzle.

Color words that begin with **t**  red .

Color words that begin with **b** yellow .

Color words that begin with **s** blue .

Color words that begin with **d** black .

 This vessel begins with s. It floats on the water. The wind blows it along. It is in the puzzle above. What is it?

What Is a Vowel?

Look at the alphabet train.
Color the **a** car red.
Color the **e** car blue.
Color the **i** car orange.
Color the **o** car purple.
Color the **u** car green.
Color the **y** car yellow.

There are 26 letters in the alphabet. Five of the letters are **vowels**. They are *a, e, i, o,* and *u.* Sometimes the letter *y* can be a vowel.

Look at each store sign.
Circle each vowel you can find. There are 13 of them.

Abby's Apples

Abby loves to eat red apples. Help Abby find the apples that have pictures with the short-*a* sound. Color these apples red. If the picture does not have a short-*a* sound, color the apple green.

Each vowel has a short sound and a long sound. **Short a makes the sound** you hear at the beginning of *Abby* and *apple*.

 This reptile looks like a crocodile, only smaller. It swims in the water. It begins with the short-*a* sound. What is it?

Find the Rhyme

Color the things in the picture that rhyme with *rat* .

hat

trees

shirt

pants

bat

mat

cat

 Think of two words that rhyme with *rat* that are not in the picture.

Hop Along

Help Tad Frog find his way to his friends across the pond. Color the pictures that rhyme with **pad** green.

 Color the other pictures red.

Special Delivery

Help make the delivery to the store.
Follow the pictures that rhyme with *van* .

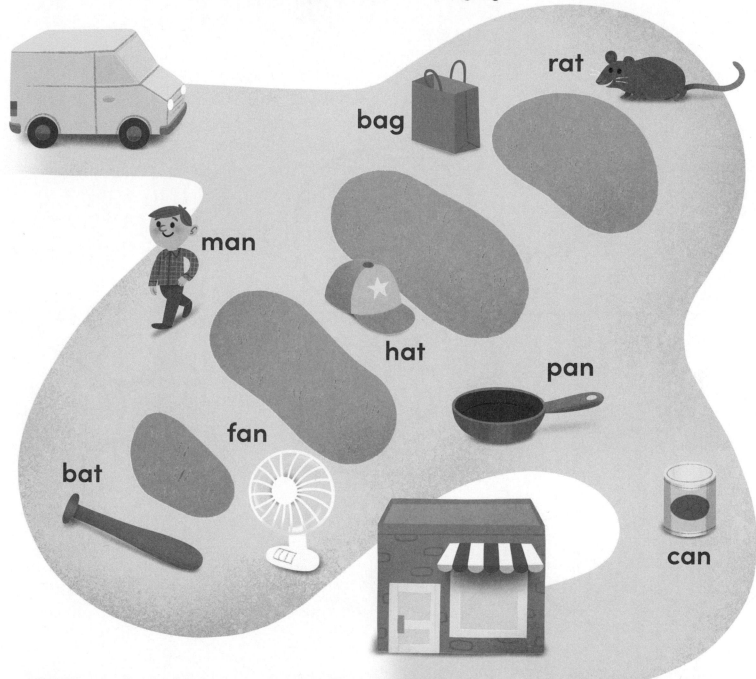

 Count how many cans of soup you have at home.

Don't Step on the Tack!

Find and color the pictures that rhyme with *back* .

snack   tack   sack   crack

 Think of two more words that rhyme with *back*. On another sheet of paper, draw a picture of one of them.

Picture This!

In each row, color the picture that rhymes with the first picture.

fan	hat	pan	glad
bat	man	sad	cat
sad	mad	rat	fan
sack	can	van	backpack

Rhyming Tic-Tac-Toe

Look at each game board. Name the pictures. Find and color 3 pictures on each game board that rhyme. Look ←, ↓, and ↘.

© Scholastic Inc.

Ed's Eggs

It is time for Ed to gather the eggs. Help Ed find the eggs that have pictures with the short-*e* sound. Color these eggs brown. If the picture does not have the short-*e* sound, leave the egg white.

Short e makes the sound you hear at the beginning of *Ed* and *egg*.

 When you say this word you nod your head up and down. It means the opposite of *no*. It has the short-*e* sound. What word is it?

Farmer Ben

Color things in the picture that rhyme with *den* .

hen   pen   ten   men

Watch Out!

Help Ted find his way down the hill without hitting the shed. Follow the pictures that rhyme with *shed* .

red

bed

hen

bell

nest

pen

sled

shell

well

Finish

Taking the Pet to the Vet

Name each picture below.
Color the pictures that rhyme with **met** .

jet

pet

hen

sled

net

wet

bed

pen

vet

Show and Tell

Read the story with a grown-up.
Find and color the picture words in the story that rhyme with *tell.*

bell   shell   yell   well

It was time for Show and Tell. Bobby was so excited,

he began to 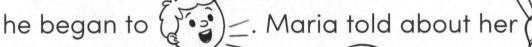. Maria told about her .

Leigh brought her favorite . Ted showed a picture

of a wishing 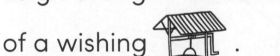.

Flower Power

Color the pictures that rhyme with **sled** red.

Color the pictures that rhyme with **ten** yellow.

Color the pictures that rhyme with **yell** blue.

Color the pictures that rhyme with **net** orange.

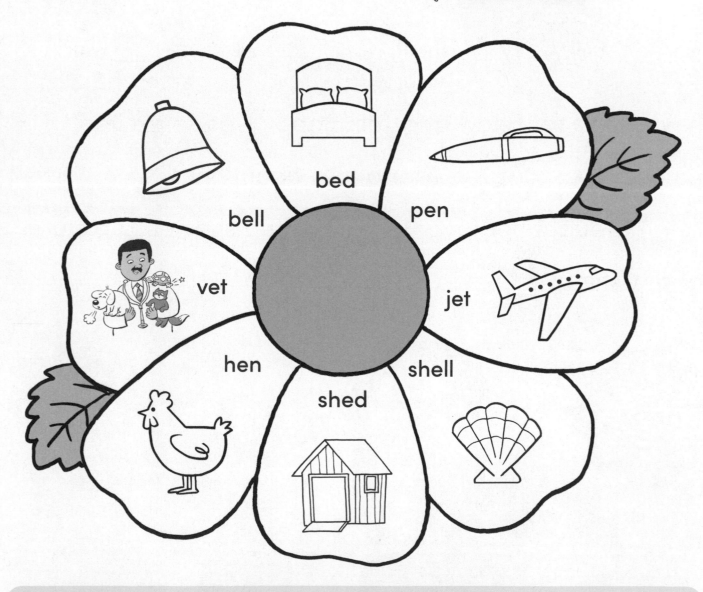

bell · bed · pen · vet · jet · hen · shed · shell

⭐ On another sheet of paper, draw a flower with four petals. On each petal, draw something with a short-*e* sound.

Igloo Inn

Welcome to the Igloo Inn. Color the space around the pictures with the short-*i* sound blue. If the picture does not have a short-*i* sound, draw an **X** on it.

Strike!

See how many bowling pins you can knock down.
Mark an **X** on the ones that rhyme with *pin* 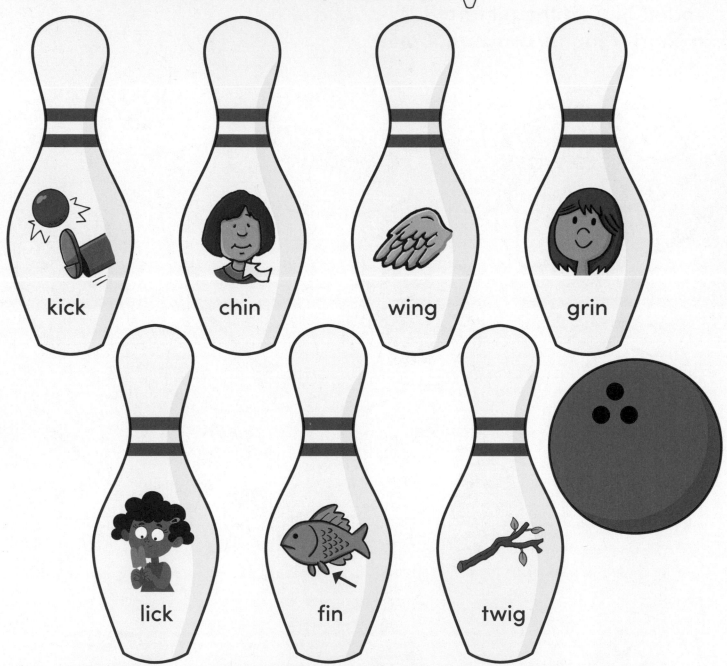.

kick

chin

wing

grin

lick

fin

twig

Name two more words that rhyme with *pin*.

Going to the Pig Shindig

Read the story with a grown-up.
Find and color the picture words in the story that rhyme with *big*.

pig   wig   twig   big

Once there was a [pig] who wanted to go to the

[big] shindig. She put on her pretty pink [wig] .

The [wig] was way too [big] . On the way to the

shindig, the [wig] got caught on a [twig] . The [pig]

nearly lost her [wig] .

Fit for a King

On the crown, color the pictures that rhyme with *king* .

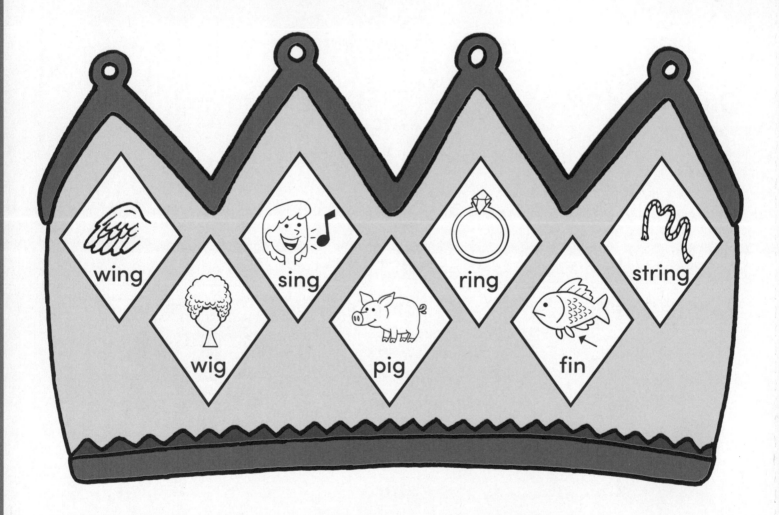

wing

wig

sing

pig

ring

fin

string

 Tell a story about a king and other things that have the *-ing* sound.

Where's the Rhyme?

Name each picture.
Color the pictures that rhyme with *lick* .

pig

king

kick

ring

sick

wig

grin

sing

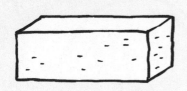

brick

chick

chin

twig

Oliver's Olives

Oliver likes to put green olives in his salad. Help Oliver find the olives that have pictures with the short-**o** sound. Color these olives green. If the picture does not have the short-**o** sound, color the olive black.

Freddy the Frog

Read the story with a grown-up.
Find and color the picture words in the story that rhyme with *jog*.

frog **log** **dog** **hog**

Freddy is a very large bull 🐸. He is as big as a
🪵. His best friends are a bull 🐕 and a 🐷.
Together they play leap 🐸. See them jump over
the 🪵.

Under the Big Top

Name each picture. Color the pictures that rhyme with *pop* .

mop

hop

dog

pot

STOP
stop

top

lock

 On another sheet of paper, draw a picture about this sentence: Mop up the soda pop.

Dot the Robot

Find and circle the things in the big picture that rhyme with
knot 🪢.

pot   spot   hot

Sherlock's Clues

Help Sherlock find the way to the missing lock.
Color the pictures that rhyme with **clock**  .

clock

sock

log

dog

mop

rock

knock

hog

pot

spot

block

lock

My Uncle's Umbrella

My uncle needs a new umbrella! Help him find the umbrellas that have pictures with the short-*u* sound. Color these umbrellas with red and blue stripes. If the picture does not have the short-*u* sound, write **NO** on the umbrella.

Short u makes the sound you hear at the beginning of *uncle* and *umbrella*.

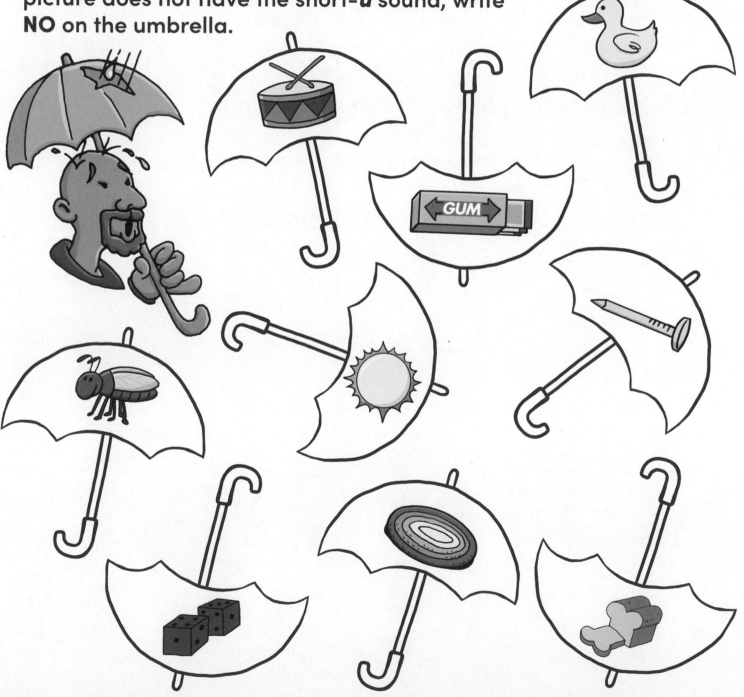

Let's Dance!

Read the story with a grown-up.
Find and color the picture words in the story that rhyme with *dug*.

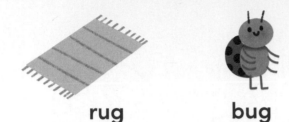

rug   bug   mug   hug

Once there was a lady . She liked to dance on

a ⬛. Her favorite dance was the jitter 🐛. She won

a first-place ☕. Everyone gave her a 🐞🐞 for being

the best dancing lady 🐛.

© Scholastic Inc.

Hit a Home Run!

Randy hit a home run.
Start at home plate and color the bases that rhyme with *fun* .

The Stuck Duck

Help the duck across the pond.
Color the pictures that rhyme with **duck.**

sun

truck

bun

puck

hug

rug

duck

mug

bug

yuck

run

Rhyme and Color

Color the pictures that rhyme with *luck* yellow.
Color the pictures that rhyme with *rug* blue.
Color the pictures that rhyme with *run* orange.

sun

bird

boy

hug

shell

ball

duck

bun

truck

shoes

mug

bug

Short-Vowel Crosswords

Use the picture clues to add a short vowel to each puzzle.

Short-Vowel Tic-Tac-Toe

Name the pictures. Find and color 3 pictures on each game board with the same short-vowel sound. Look ←, ↓, and ↘.

1 Short-*a* sound as in

2 Short-*i* sound as in

3 Short-*e* sound as in

4 Short-*u* sound as in

City C and Country C

Look at each picture below. If the picture begins with an **s** sound, as in *city*, circle **s**. If the picture begins with a **k** sound, as in *country*, circle **k**.

C can make two sounds. If the vowels **e** or **i** come after the **c**, then **c** will have the **s** sound. If one of the other vowels (**a, o, u**) comes after the **c**, then **c** will have the **k** sound.

corn	cent	cereal	coat

k s	k s	k s	k s

cake	ceiling	cow	cat

k s	k s	k s	k s

celery	coconut	circles	comb
		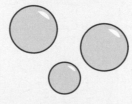	
k s	k s	k s	k s

Use the words from the previous page.

Write each word that begins with the same sound as *city.*

_____   _____   _____

_____   _____   _____

_____   _____   _____

Write each word that begins with the same sound as *country.*

_____   _____   _____

_____   _____   _____

Gary the Goat and George the Giraffe

Look at each picture below. If the picture begins with a **g** sound, as in *goat*, circle **g**. If the picture begins with a **j** sound, as in *giraffe*, circle **j**.

G can make two sounds. Some words that begin with g make the same sound that you hear in *Gary* and *goat*. But sometimes a **g** can sound like a j, as in *George* and *giraffe*.

gate	girl	gingerbread	gift

g j	g j	g j	g j

giant	guitar	gum	gerbil

g j	g j	g j	g j

goose	gorilla	general	gymnast

g j	g j	g j	g j

Use the words from the previous page.

Write each word that begins with the same sound as *Gary*.

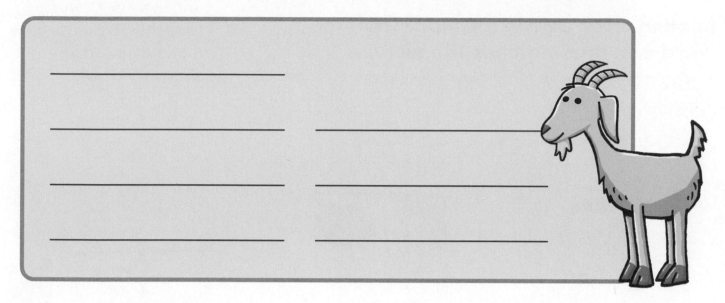

Write each word that begins with the same sound as *George*.

Queen Q and Her Helper U

In each crown, write the word from the Word Box that matches the picture.

Queen Q is very special. She has a helper named U. When Queen Q and Helper U work together, they make a sound that sounds like *kw*.

Word Box

question   quiet   quarrel
quarter   quack   quail   quilt

Superhero X to the Rescue

Help Superhero X put the missing **x** in each word. Then draw a line to the matching picture.

X makes the sound of **ks**. Most of the time, an **x** is in the middle or at the end of a word.

fo____

mi____er

ta____i

e____it

a____

si____

o____

bo____

e____ercise

tu____edo

 ⭐ It begins with *x*. It is a special kind of picture that a doctor takes so that she can see your bones. What is it?

Animal Tails

Name each animal.
Write the ending sound in the box by its tail.

Consonants can come at the beginning, middle, or end of a word.

 This creature lives in the sea. It has six arms and two legs. Its head looks like a balloon. It ends with s. What is it? On another sheet of paper, draw one eating eight candy canes.

Larry Last

Help Larry Last find the last sound that each word makes.
Circle the correct letter under each lunchbox.

k   n   s   r   g   l   s   f   r

n   d   z   b   m   n   t   k   p

n   f   d   m   x   r   g   z   l

d   v   r   l   k   d   g   t   f

Consonant Caboose

Find and color two words on each train that end with the same sound. Then, write the letter of the ending sound in the caboose.

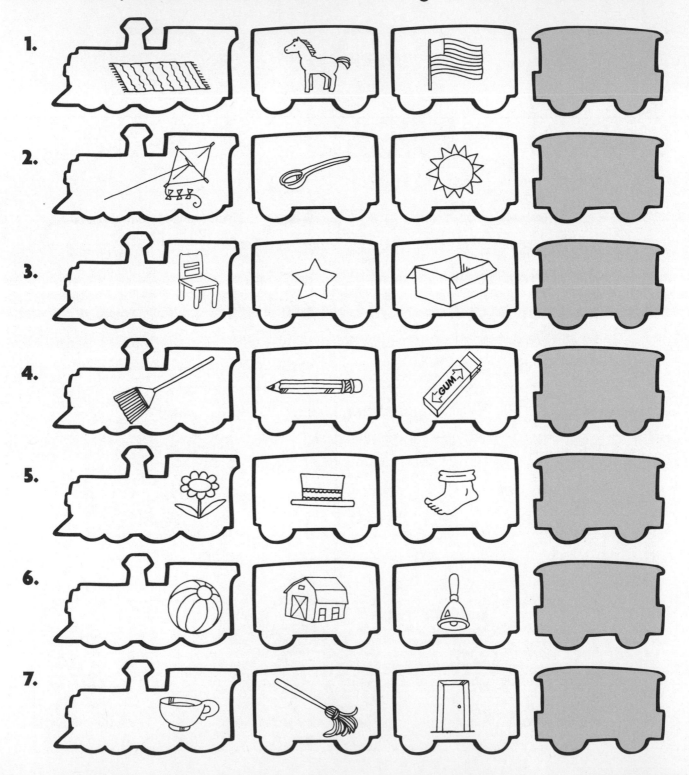

© Scholastic Inc.

What Do You See?

Say the words. Listen for the ending sounds.
Use the color key to make a picture.

blue = s	green = t	black = d	red = l	white = m

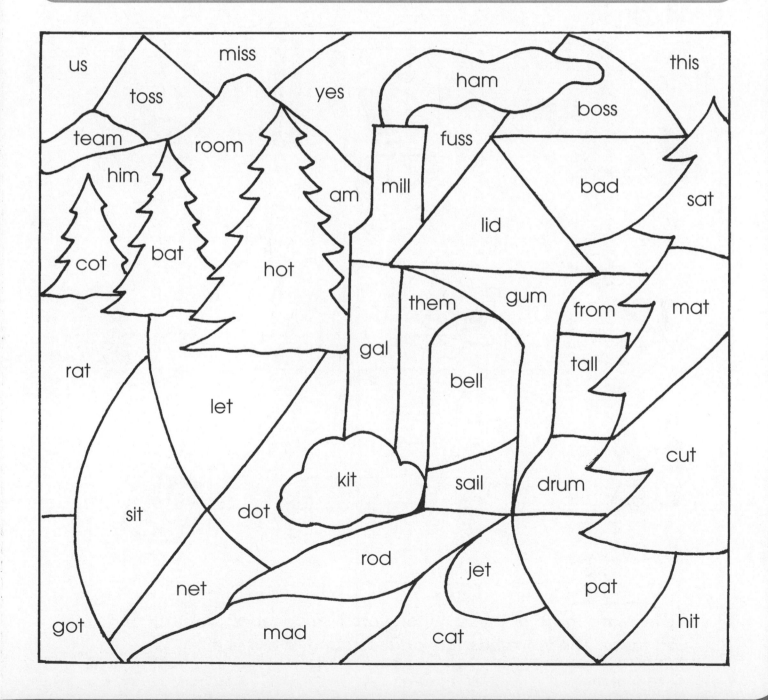

Amy's Aprons

Amy needs a new apron. Help Amy find the aprons that have pictures with the long-*a* sound. Color these aprons pink. If the picture on an apron does not have a long-*a* sound, color it purple.

Every vowel has a long sound and a short sound. **Long a** makes the sound you hear at the beginning of *Amy* and *apron*.

 There are three of these. When you hit a baseball, you run and step on them. The word has the long-*a* sound. What is it?

Don't Forget Your Skates!

Find and color the things that rhyme with *ate* .

plate

skate

gate

⭐ Say a name that rhymes with *ate*.

Jake the Snake

Color the pictures below that rhyme with *snake.*

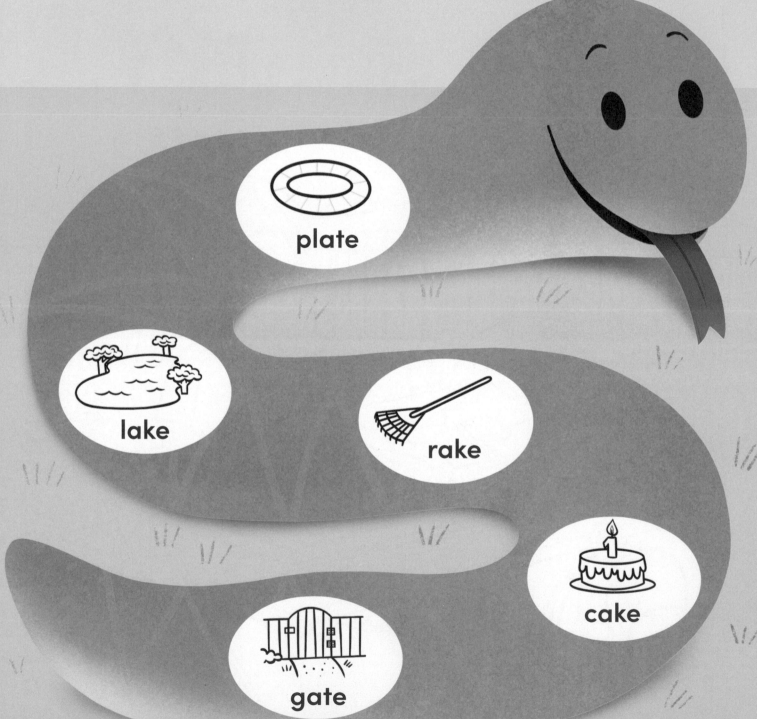

plate

lake

rake

cake

gate

A Day at the Beach

Read the story with a grown-up.
Find and color the picture words in the story that rhyme with **nail**.

pail   trail   snail   nail   sail

Sam walked down the [trail]. He looked for things to

put in his [pail]. The first thing Sam saw was a [nail].

He picked up the [nail] and put it in his [pail]. Farther

down the [trail] Sam saw a [snail]. He put the [snail] in

the [pail]. Sam had room for one more thing in his [pail].

Lying on the [trail] was a boat with a broken [sail].

Color the Rhyme

Color the pictures that rhyme with *lake*  **red**.

Color the pictures that rhyme with *ate* **yellow**.

Color the pictures that rhyme with *sail* **blue**.

snail

gate

pail

snake

cake

nail

plate

rake

⭐ On another sheet of paper, draw a picture of something else that rhymes with *snail*.

Ethan Eagle

Ethan Eagle is lonely. He needs a friend. Help Ethan find the eagles that have pictures with the long-*e* sound. Color these eagles brown. If the picture on an eagle does not have a long-*e* sound, write **NO** on it.

Long e makes the sound you hear at the beginning of *Ethan* and *eagle*.

What Do You See at the Park?

Color the things in the picture that rhyme with *see*.

bee   knee   **3**   tree

 On another sheet of paper, draw a picture of something that makes you shout with glee.

Beep, Beep

In each row, cross out the pictures that do not rhyme with *beep.*

bell

jeep

knee

sheep

shell

tree

three

jet

sleep

hen

shed

sweep

 Name the nursery rhyme that tells about a girl who lost her sheep.

Ivan's Ice

It is so hot today! Ivan needs some ice in his drink. Help Ivan find the ice cubes that have pictures with the long-*i* sound. Outline these ice cubes in blue. If the picture on an ice cube does not have a long-*i* sound, draw an **X** over it.

Long i makes the sound you hear at the beginning of *Ivan* and *ice*.

 This is something your lips do when you are happy. It is another word for *grin*. It has the long-*i* sound. What is it? On another sheet of paper, draw a picture of your face with one of these on it.

© Scholastic Inc.

Be Mine!

Color the hearts with pictures that rhyme with *valentine* .

vine

hive

nine

9

line

ice

pine

Be
Mine

 Make a valentine card that says *Be Mine!* **Give it to someone special.**

For the Right Price

Find and color the things that rhyme with *price* .

mice

string

rice

ice

button

vine

dice

cheese

Buzzy Bees

Help the bees find their way back home.
Follow the pictures that rhyme with **hive** .

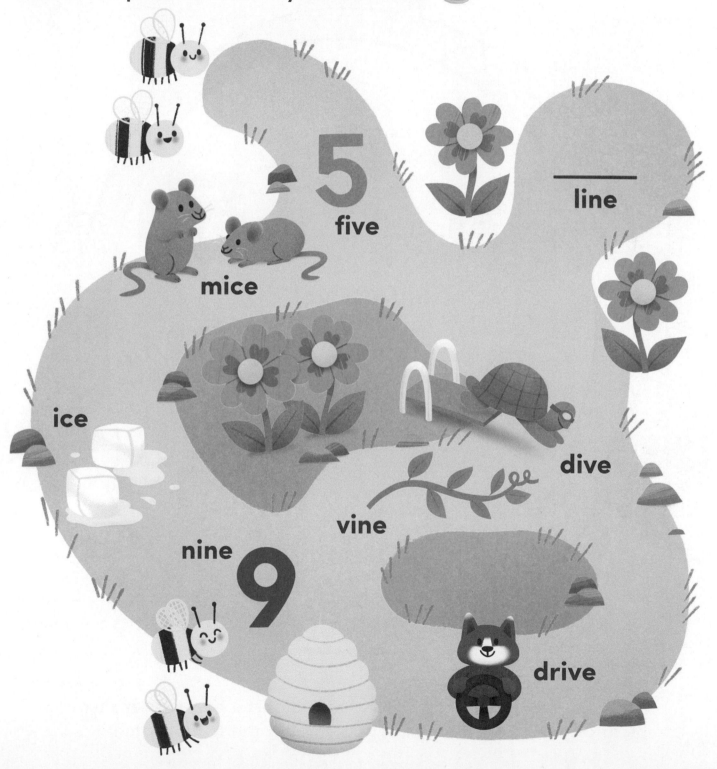

Rhyme Time

Draw lines to connect the pictures that rhyme.

 Make your own rhyming watch. Think of three new sets of rhyming pictures. On another sheet of paper, draw them in a watch.

Miss Opal's Ovals

Miss Opal is teaching her class about shapes. Today they learned about ovals. Draw an oval around the pictures that have the long-**o** sound. If the picture does not have a long-**o** sound, draw a square around it.

Long **o** makes the sound you hear at the beginning of *Opal* and *oval*.

oval

Construction Zone

Help the digger fill the right dump trucks.
Color the trucks that have pictures that rhyme with *stone* .

© Scholastic Inc.

Row, Row, Row Your Boat

Help the rowboat find the shore.
Color the pictures that rhyme with *float* ▬▬.

coat

goat

cone

phone

nose

throat

Mighty Firefighter

Help the firefighter put out the fire.
Color the pictures in the windows that rhyme with **hose** blue.
Color the other windows red.

Unicorn University

This unicorn is smart! She goes to Unicorn University. Find every book that has a picture with the long-*u* sound. Color these books blue. If the picture does not have a long-*u* sound, draw an **X** on it.

Long u makes the sound you hear at the beginning of *unicorn* and *university*.

 This is the name of a country. It is made up of 50 states. Its president lives in Washington, D.C. The first word in the name begins with a long-*u* sound. What country is it?

Long-u Word Fruit

Look at the word on each piece of fruit. Fill in the blank to make a rhyming word. Read your words to a friend.

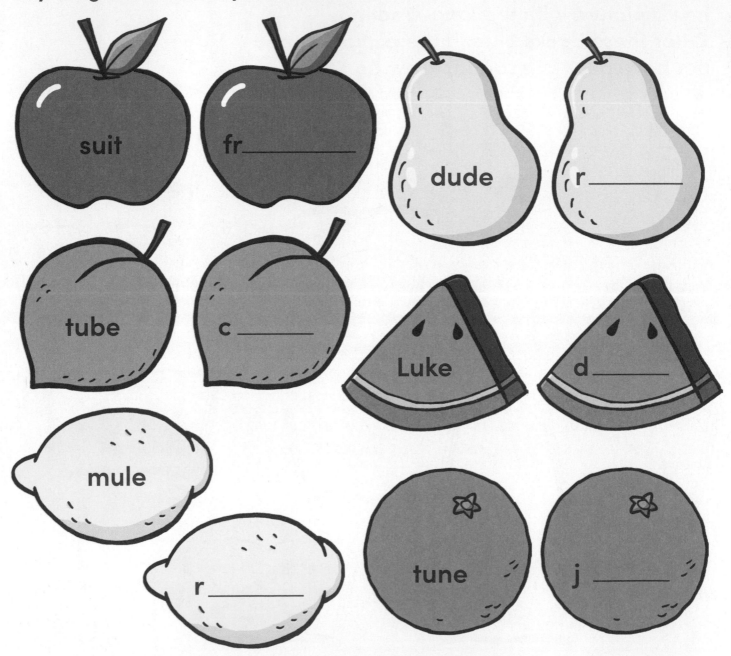

suit

fr_____

dude

r_____

tube

c_____

Luke

d_____

mule

r_____

tune

j_____

 This is the color of the sky and the sea. It has a long-*u* sound. What is it? Think of something else that is this color. On another sheet of paper, draw and color it.

Long-Vowel Tic-Tac-Toe

Name the pictures. Find and color 3 pictures on each game board with the same long-vowel sound. Look ←, ↓, and ↘.

1. Long-*e* sound

2. Long-*i* sound

3. Long-*o* sound

4. Long-*a* sound

Time for Rhymes

Name each picture. In each set, circle the pictures that rhyme.

Check the Signs

Name each picture.
In each row, circle the picture that rhymes with the first picture.

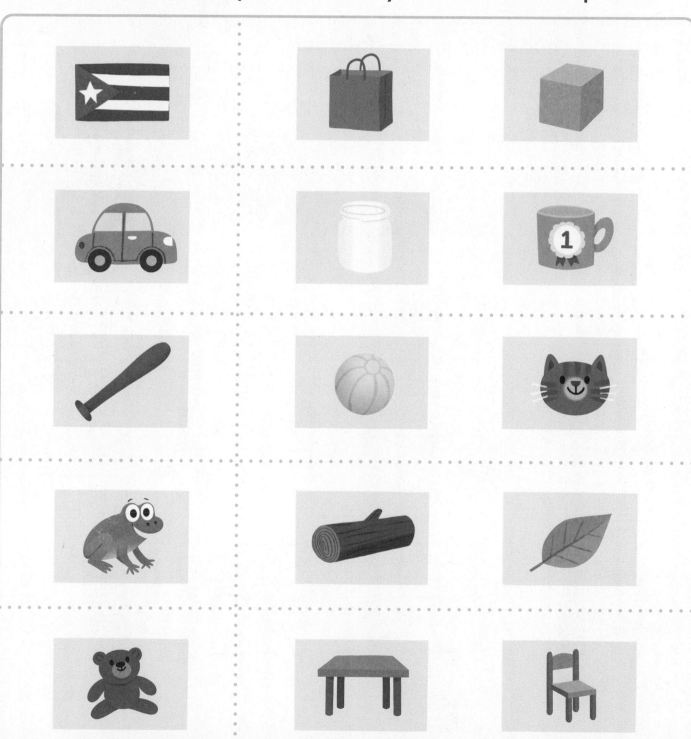

Be a Word Builder!

Make your own rhyming words.
Look at each picture and say the word.
Copy the word. Then, change the first
letter using each letter on the hammer
to make new words.

p s r m f h b

h c m t w f

f j l h

s l b

cat

ball

dog

hand

© Scholastic Inc.

· SCHOLASTIC SUCCESS WITH ·

SCIENCE

Healthy Treats to Eat

Fruits and **vegetables** help our bodies grow big and strong. Name each picture. Then follow the fruits and vegetables to move through the maze.

 Name your favorite fruit and vegetable.

What Do Bears Eat?

Circle the things that bears eat.

Winter Sleepers

The animals below **hibernate**, or sleep, in the winter.
Name them. Then, find them in the big picture.

turtle   chipmunk   bear   frog   bat   snake

Nocturnal Animals

Nocturnal animals stay awake at night. Can you find 5 nocturnal animals? (Circle) them. Then, color the picture.

Inside a Chipmunk's Burrow

Look at the diagram. Then, follow the directions below.

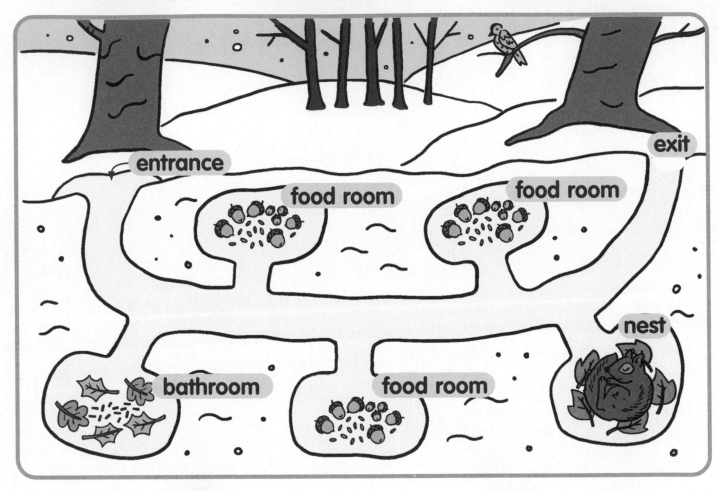

entrance · exit · food room · food room · food room · bathroom · nest

1. (Circle) the .

   chipmunk

2. Put ✔s on the .

   food rooms

3. Put an ✘ on the .

   bathroom

4. Put a ☺ on the entrance.

Armored (With Shell) or Not!

Some animals with hard shells are called **crustaceans**.
Color the animals that have shells.

Rough Reptiles

Animals covered with rough, dry skin belong to the **reptile** family. Trace to make reptiles. Color.

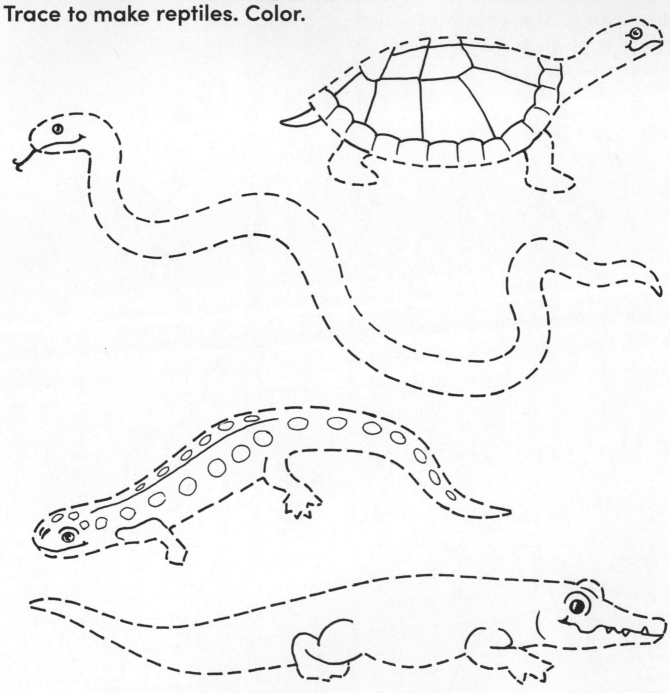

 Name each reptile.

Mammal Mix-Up

Animals with hair or fur belong to the **mammal** family.
Mark an **X** on the animals in each row that do not belong
to the mammal family.

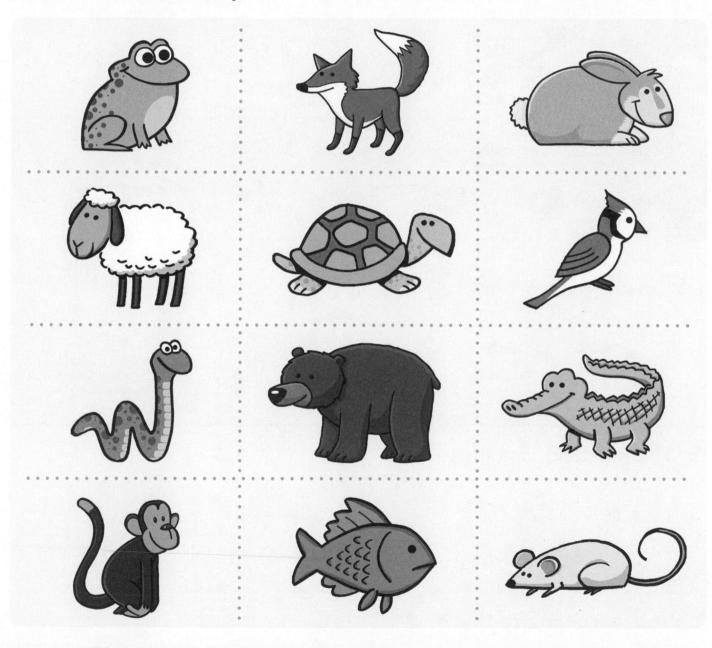

 Did you know that you are a mammal? On another sheet of paper,
draw a picture of you and your favorite mammals.

Tracks in the Snow

This chart shows what some animal tracks look like. Circle the answer to each question.

	deer	dog	rabbit
animal			
track			

1. Whose tracks are these?

2. Whose tracks are these?

3. Whose tracks are these?

Shark Diagram

A **diagram** shows the parts of something. The labels name the parts. Draw the missing parts on the shark. Then, trace the words to make labels.

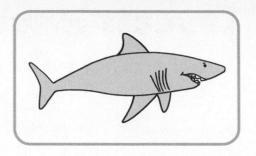

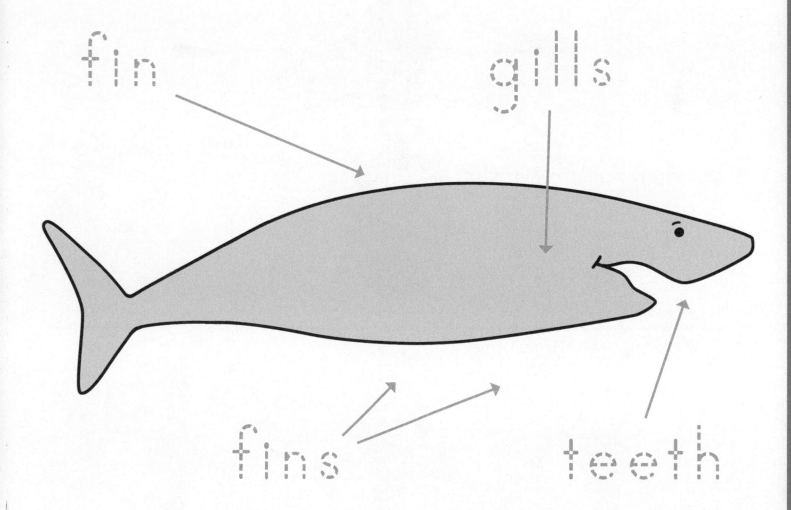

fin

gills

fins

teeth

Insects Have Six Legs

An ant is an **insect**. Count its legs.

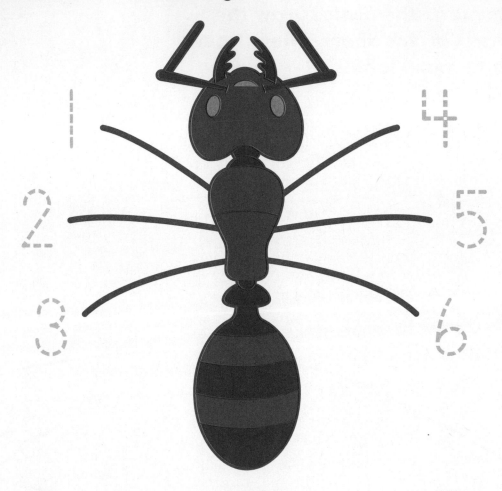

Draw six legs on each of these ants.

Bird Body Diagram

Label each part of the bird to complete the diagram.
Use the words in the Word Bank.

Word Bank

beak
eye
wing
tail
foot

Plants Grow Above and Below

Read the sentences and finish the pictures.

Stems and leaves grow up. Draw the leaves.	**Tree trunks grow up. Draw the trunk.**	**Carrot leaves grow up. Draw the leaves.**
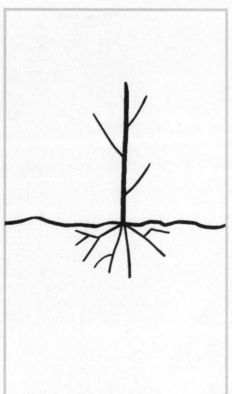	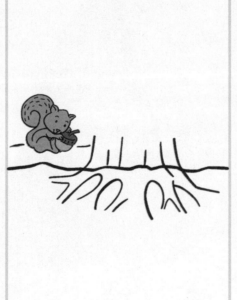	
Roots grow down. Draw more roots.	**Tree roots grow down. Draw more roots.**	**Carrots grow down. Draw the carrot.**

A Carrot Grows

How does a carrot grow?
Number the pictures to show the order.

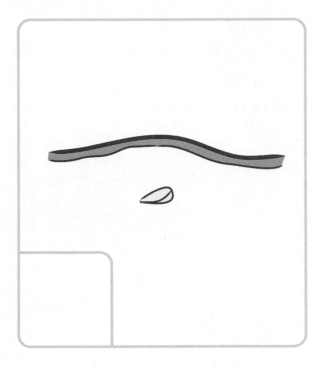

What Do Plants Need?

Draw lines from the plant to the pictures of things that it needs to live.

water

cookies

air

sun

hat

soil

Signs of Spring

Circle the things you see in the spring.

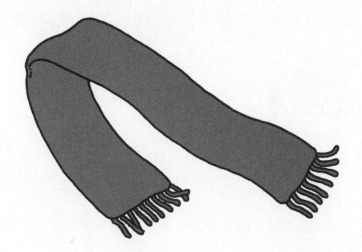

Signs of Fall

Circle the things you see in the fall.

Weather Outside My Window

Read each weather word. Draw what you would see out your window in that kind of weather.

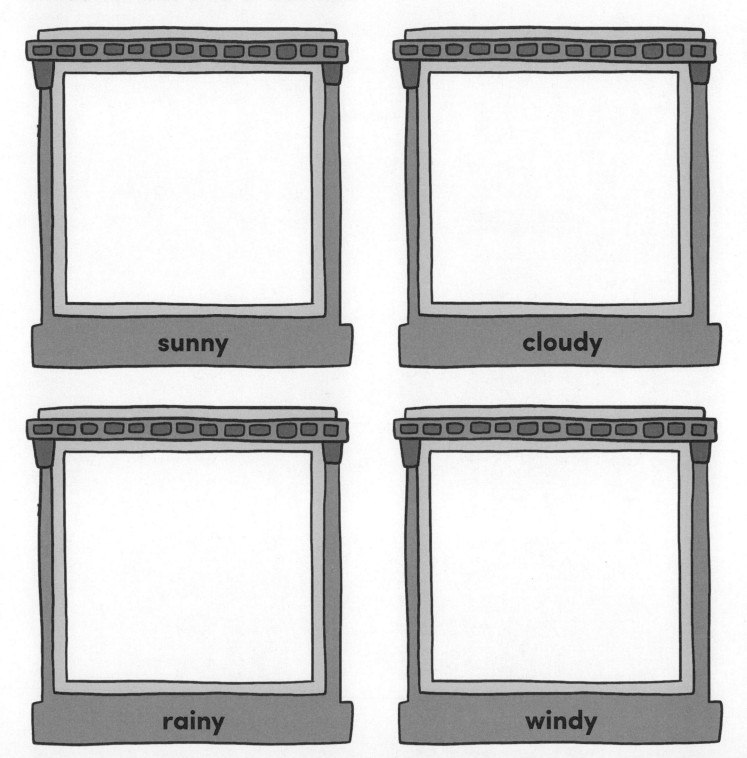

sunny

cloudy

rainy

windy

Can Wind Move It?

Make wind by blowing through a straw!
Predict which objects your wind will move. Then find out.

	YES 👍	NO 👎
cotton ball		
crayon		
block		
leaf		
rock		
tissue box		
Draw your own item.		
Draw your own item.		

· SCHOLASTIC SUCCESS WITH ·

ITTY-BITTY
WORD BOOKS

How to Assemble the Word Books

1. Tear out each page along the perforation.

2. Cut along the dashed lines; fold along the solid lines.

3. Place the pages in order and staple along the spine.

I live in

_____

16

traffic
light

14

post office

12

car

10

My Little Neighborhood

house

3

firehouse

5

police officer

7

school

2

school bus

15

store

4

stop sign

13

police station

6

mail carrier

11

firefighter

8

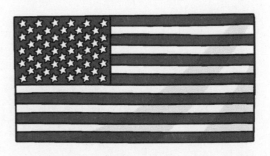

flag

9

scarecrow

16

My Little Book of
FARM WORDS

goat

14

cow

3

grain

12

sheep

5

tractor

10

horse

7

barn

2

farmer

15

rooster

4

chicken

13

MILK **milk**

6

egg

11

duck

8

pig

9

I made this mini-book
in the month of

_____

16

Month-by-Month
Mini-Book

New Year

14

February

3

November

12

April

5

September

10

June

7

January

2

seasons

15

March

4

December

13

May

6

October

11

July

8

August

9

My favorite fruit

_____

My favorite vegetable

_____

16

My Tiny Book of
Fruits & Vegetables

corn

14

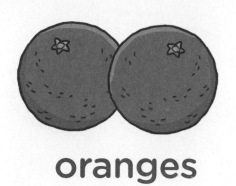

oranges

3

broccoli

12

banana

5

pears

10

watermelon

7

apples

2

celery

15

lemons

4

peas

13

strawberries

6

carrot

11

pineapple

8

grapes

9

My favorite way to
travel is by

_____

16

LET'S GO!
Transportation Words

wagon

14

bus

3

truck

12

plane

5

running

10

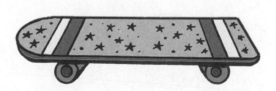

skateboard

7

 © Scholastic Inc.

car

2

rocket

15

train

4

van

13

bike

6

scooter

11

ship

8

walking

9

My favorite
big animal is

_____

16

ostrich

14

polar bear

3

dinosaur

12

whale

5

tiger

10

jaguar

7

elephant

2

camel

15

rhinoceros

4

panda

13

horse

6

zebra

11

buffalo

8

moose

9

© Scholastic Inc.

I would like a/an

_____

for a pet.

16

My Mini-Book of
PETS

iguana

14

dog

3

snake

12

gerbil

5

parakeet

10

mouse

7

cat

2

frog

4

hamster

6

fish

8

imaginary pet

15

rabbit

13

parrot

11

turtle

9

Right now I feel

_____

16

Feelings & Faces

angry

14

sad

3

silly

12

mad

5

sleepy

10

worried

7

frustrated

2

funny face

15

happy

4

calm

13

content

6

nervous

11

surprised

8

excited

9

© Scholastic Inc.

My favorite shape is

_____

16

A Small Book of Shapes

heart

14

square

3

cone

oval

12

5

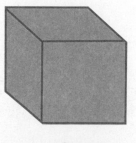

cube

octagon

10

7

circle

2

rectangle

4

triangle

6

diamond

8

cylinder

15

pentagon

13

hexagon

11

star

9

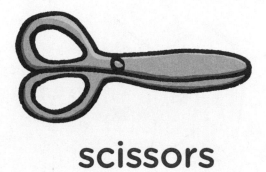

crayons

16

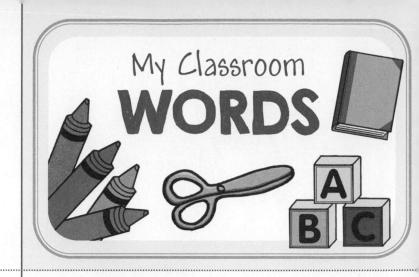

scissors

14

chair

3

door

12

teacher

5

clock

10

book

7

 desk

2

 blocks

15

 easel

4

 map

13

 student

6

 glue

11

 notebook

8

 pencil

9

My favorite color is

_____

16

Rainbow
in Your Pocket!

markers

14

green

3

paints

12

blue

5

black

10

brown

7

 red

2

 yellow

4

 orange

6

 purple

8

 white

15

 crayons

13

 rainbow

11

 pink

9

© Scholastic Inc.

USING THE FLASH CARDS

Sight words are the most frequently used words in any text. Sight words include words such as *the, of, to, are, so, how,* and *when.* Using these flash cards just minutes a day will help your child commit these all-important words to memory, building a firm foundation to read with ease.

Use this simple routine to introduce five sight words at a time.

1. Share the card and read the word aloud, slowly and clearly.
2. Have your child read each letter in the sight word. Then, have him or her read the word to you.

to

the

in

of

is

and

you

a

that

on

3. Discuss the sight word and how to use it.
4. Use the sight word in a sentence.
5. Then, invite your child to use the sight word in a sentence.
6. Move onto a new sight word and follow the same routine.
7. After you and your child have gone through all the sight words, shuffle them. Then, have your child select a card at random, read it, and use it in a sentence.
8. If your child struggles with a particular sight word, spend additional time on it and/or revisit it in another session.

are

it

as

he

with

was

they

for

I	from
at	or
be	one
this	had
have	by

were	help
we	but
when	not
your	what
can	all

said	eat
there	she
use	do
an	how
here	come

many	will
then	up
them	little
these	away
so	out

some	him
would	into
make	play
like	has
	look

some

him

her

into

would

play

make

has

like

look

good	two
no	please
our	write
could	go
saw	see